"I'm Surprised
You Care for Traditions!"

"I don't, unless they suit my purpose," he answered, staring down at her, his gaze direct and piercing. Then, before she could stop him, he pulled her to him and held her tightly.

"Aren't you forgetting your promise?" she remonstrated.

"You're very beautiful, Kit," he said softly. "Very beautiful. And I want you more than I have ever wanted anyone."

"You promised," she said weakly.

"I know I did, and I've kept that promise for a month. Are you sure you really want me to keep it now?" His mouth grazed her cheek and moved closer to hers. . . .

ANN MAJOR
is not only a successful author, she also manages a business and runs a busy household with three small children. Among her many interests she lists traveling and playing the piano—her favorite composer, quite naturally, the romantic Chopin.

Dear Reader:

At Silhouette we try to publish books with you, our reader, in mind, and we're always trying to think of something new. We're very pleased to announce the creation of Silhouette First Love, a new line of contemporary romances written by the very finest young adult writers especially for our twelve-to-sixteen-year-old readers. First Love has many of the same elements you've enjoyed in Silhouette Romances—love stories, happy endings and the same attention to detail and description—but features heroines and situations with which our younger readers can more easily identify.

First Love from Silhouette will be available in bookstores this October. We will introduce First Love with six books, and each month thereafter we'll bring you two new First Love romances.

We welcome any suggestions or comments, and I invite you to write to us at the address below.

Karen Solem
Editor-in-Chief
Silhouette Books
P.O. Box 769
New York, N.Y. 10019

ANN MAJOR
Wild
Lady

Silhouette Romance

Published by Silhouette Books New York

America's Publisher of Contemporary Romance

*To Nancy Jackson—for her
enthusiastic and very expert
help with this project.*

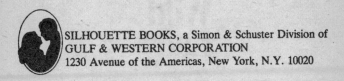

SILHOUETTE BOOKS, a Simon & Schuster Division of
GULF & WESTERN CORPORATION
1230 Avenue of the Americas, New York, N.Y. 10020

Copyright © 1981 by Ann Major

Distributed by Pocket Books

ISBN: 0-671-57090-0

First Silhouette printing July, 1981

10 9 8 7 6 5 4 3 2 1

America's Publisher of Contemporary Romance

Printed in the U.S.A.

Chapter One

The black-haired, black-eyed beauty smiled mockingly in the foot-high photograph on the society page of the *Corpus Christi Chat* beneath the sensational headline, "Oilman's Daughter Stranded at Altar." With trembling fingers, Kit gripped the paper even more tightly as she critically studied her own picture for a second time.

How had she managed that picture—the radiant smile, the sparkling eyes? The photograph depicted a young girl glowing with expectation at the prospect of marriage. Had she ever really been that girl?

She skimmed the article beneath. "Kit Jackson, daughter of wealthy South Texas oil operator, Howard Jackson, waited in vain last night for her bridegroom, Rodney Starr, to make his appearance . . ."

Oh! The paper made it sound so tragic! Everyone who read the article would think Rodney had deliberately stood her up! They would think that she herself was heartbroken! But it wasn't like that . . ."

"If they only knew how relieved I really am," she said half-aloud. "If they only knew . . ."

"Relief!" Surely it was the sweetest word in the English language just as it was the sweetest sensation she'd felt for a long time.

She remembered the long months of tension that had preceded the events of last night. Her family and his pressuring them both into their decision. Once she'd agreed to marry him, plans for the grand, society wedding had been like an avalanche sweeping Rodney and her along. Neither of them had known how to stop things. Lavish parties, gifts, balls. . . . Occasionally across a crowded ballroom she'd caught an almost desperate look in Rodney's eyes, and surely he'd seen the same look in hers. She'd wanted to call the wedding off; she'd come close to doing it many times. But once the marriage plans had been set in motion, she'd lacked the courage.

Newspaper articles covering their engagement had made it sound like a fairytale marriage—the handsome heir to the Starr cattle and ranching fortune marrying the wealthy Jackson beauty.

She had never loved Rodney in the way a wife should love the man she planned to marry, although she was very fond of him. She had only drifted into a relationship with him on the rebound because of her devastating romance with the one man she'd truly loved.

Black print blurred and the paper fell from her hands to rest beside her untouched breakfast tray. The breeze gusting up from the bay caught its edges and they fluttered. She arose, clutching the wrought-iron railing that laced her balcony overlooking the grounds.

Beneath her billowed nine hundred yards of gaily-striped yellow and white canvas, the party tent the caterers had rented from some local outfit her father said was owned and run by a "brash young upstart" who'd insisted on being paid in advance for his rental, even from the Jacksons. As if the Jacksons were no better or worse than anyone else. She saw the rented tiki torches, the tables, chairs, the unused bandstand—everything set up with such care for the reception that had never been.

Last night came back to her. If she lived to be a hundred, Kit would never be able to forget it.

She'd dressed carefully—to be appropriately beautiful on her wedding day. She'd been swathed from head to toe in designer lace that scratched her flesh everywhere it touched. She'd been imprisoned in that stuffy dressing room with her mother, who mildly nervous at first had become frantic an hour later when there was still no Rodney. Kit, however, had had just the opposite reaction. When she was informed that Rodney was late, she'd felt the first glimmer of hope. Then when that first hour had passed without his coming, she'd decided that even if he did arrive she would have to summon her own courage and call the wedding off no matter how she disappointed and humiliated her mother and father before their society friends.

Two tortuous hours passed before Rodney called. By that time the hum in the sanctuary had grown to a deafening buzz. Kit's mother took the call in the minister's office and returned with the news she'd delivered with false brightness.

"Don't worry, *mi querida* . . ." Anitra Jackson had begun, lapsing, because she was nervous, into her native language, Spanish.

"Where's Rodney? What happened?" Kit blurted.

"There's been a little accident . . . a car wreck

. . . Rodney's in the hospital . . . nothing serious . . . whiplash . . . He'll stay overnight in the hospital for observation . . ."

Kit's first concern had been for Rodney. What if he were really seriously injured? Her mother had at last managed to reassure her that his injuries were only minor. Relief had swamped her like a joyous flood, but she'd managed to conceal her true feelings from her mother. Dear Mother, she'd been so anxious that the wedding take place. Arabella Starr, Rodney's mother, was her dearest friend; a wedding linking their two families her fond dream.

"But, *querida*, we do have a problem of our own to face. The church is filled with wedding guests! What do we tell them?"

Kit had managed calmly. "The truth, Mother. I'll make the announcements to them now."

She'd stood before a thousand guests in the hushed sanctuary and somehow with legs weak from relief that she'd thought would buckle and send her sprawling—designer gown and all—but with a clear, sure voice, she'd told the crowd why Rodney hadn't come. Whip-lash! She'd felt their skepticism, their pity for her. But she'd been too wild with joy to care. Let them think the worst of her! She was free! Never again would she allow herself to be swept along by the dictates of others. She'd put too many people to trouble as a result.

She flinched, sagging against the iron railing. She gazed beneath without really seeing the turquoise pool, the glossy red tiles of the cabana roof, the acres of sloping greenery, and beyond that the concrete sea wall and the glistening bay.

Suddenly she was shivering in spite of the blazing Texas sun. She moved restlessly inside her room and threw herself across the bed. The three-carat, emerald-cut diamond caught the sunlight and flashed its blue-white fire against the sprigged wallpaper. She remembered the day Rodney had slipped the ring on her finger. If only she'd refused it. How much simpler everything would have been.

How could she ever leave this room and face everyone who had worked so hard preparing for this wedding. Her parents, the Starrs, their friends. . . . All their time, effort, and money down the drain. She felt she'd used them all because she'd been too immature to stand up for herself.

Well, that would never, never happen again! It had only happened this time because of . . . of Ted. She swallowed something that was hard and painful at the thought of *him*.

Yes, it went back five years ago to him. She'd been a young and vulnerable eighteen, a college freshman in Austin when she'd fallen wildly in love with a man almost ten years her senior—Ted. He was in his last year of law school on the GI bill.

She'd loved him blindly until the last night she'd spent in his arms. The memory of that night was still vividly, horribly etched in her mind. Saxophone music had filled his small apartment with its husky sound. Ted had wrapped her so closely in his arms he'd seemed almost a part of herself. He'd drawn her down onto his studio couch, and she'd arched wantonly toward him because his kisses had filled her with a longing she'd never known before. But when his hands had gone to the zipper at the back of her dress, she'd suddenly realized she had to stop him. Sex was a physical and spiritual commitment she believed then and believed now she owed only to her husband. She'd run from his apartment, from him. . . . He had not tried to stop her. When she'd reached the safety of her dorm room, her telephone was ringing, but she'd been too badly shaken to answer it.

Later that night when she'd recovered herself, she'd realized how foolishly immature her actions must have seemed to him. She'd tried to call him on the telephone to explain, but when she'd called, he hadn't answered.

Kit would never forget the velvet-soft tones of Letitia's voice, purring sweetly when she answered Ted's phone, "He's in bed. Are you really sure you want me to disturb him?"

Kit had choked out some reply. Letitia was a girl Ted had dated briefly before he'd met Kit. Knowing that Ted had turned to Letitia after her own abrupt departure had hurt Kit deeply. She'd felt used . . . cheated. . . . She'd realized then that any woman could satisfy his needs—it didn't matter who. She had been no more than a conquest. This realization made her decide never to see him again. No matter how much she suffered, she was better off without such a man— however attractive he was, however impossible he was to forget. And she had not forgotten him!

She had refused Ted's calls. After all, what explanation could there have been for his behavior? Eventually she'd begun seeing Rodney, an old friend from her childhood. They'd drifted into a courtship. When they'd both graduated their families and friends couldn't understand why they weren't anxious to marry.

She'd allowed herself to believe that Rodney would make a good husband. After all they came from the same kind of backgrounds. He was very good with children. She'd almost convinced herself that they could achieve a happy family life together.

Last night when he hadn't shown up, she'd realized fully how wrong she'd been. She'd never wanted marriage to him any more than he had wanted marriage to her. They had had a comfortable friendship—that was all.

Ted . . . funny . . . even after five years it still hurt to think of him. She knew he lived in Corpus now although she'd never sought him out. It seemed odd to her suddenly that she hadn't run into him somewhere. Corpus wasn't really that large a town. Still, she had been away at college most of those years, and he was married to Letitia. Perhaps, after all, it wasn't so odd.

Why was she thinking of *him* again? Of the possibility of seeing him again? Long, sooty lashes squeezed tightly shut against her flawless, olive skin. If only she could shut him out of her mind and heart as easily as she could shut her eyes. But she couldn't. A vision that was all too real of him appeared before her. He was holding her tightly to him. Copper highlights glinted in his dark auburn hair. His blue eyes sparkled with love and tender desire for her. He bent his face to hers, his mouth claiming hers in a slow, deliberate kiss. She sighed heavily and opened her slanting dark eyes. Wistfully, she brushed her soft, lips with a fingertip. She could still remember how wonderful his lips had felt. She wasn't over him. How could she have considered marrying Rodney when, incredibly, she still cared for Ted?

A fierce banging at her bedroom door disrupted the painful memory and equally painful realization.

Kit knew it must be her father, for no one else made that kind of noise this early in the morning in the house. Before she could answer, he let himself in.

He was as distinguished looking as always, dressed in immaculate, stiffly creased white slacks and a navy T-shirt open at the throat. Yachting attire. The race! She'd forgotten it entirely. But he hadn't.

He tucked his silver winged hair beneath a navy colored captain's hat—the final touch so that he looked what he was this morning—the debonair yachtsman. His gray eyes were on her—assessing.

"How're you feeling today?" He saw the pages of the newspaper on the thick pile of blue carpet—pages the wind had blown inside. He was bending over and retrieving the scattered pages. For a long moment his eyes lingered with a certain pride on her picture. "Guess I shouldn't have to ask." She was thankful there was no trace of sympathy in his voice. At least she wouldn't have to pretend with him.

"I'm doing all right."

Her answer caught him by surprise and he stared at her intently. "I can see that. I never did think Rodney was the right man for you in spite of the fact his father's an old friend of mine. Not much to the boy though, if you take away his ranch, thoroughbreds, those Santa Gertrudis, and that fancy car he drives."

"Daddy, if you thought that, why didn't you ever say . . ."

"It's not my place to make your decisions anymore, Kitten. You're old enough to make your own mistakes. Goodness knows I've made enough of my own to know how easy they are to make."

"Oh, Daddy . . ." She threw her arms around him. "I should have known you'd understand."

Slightly embarrassed by her show of affection: "I guess Rodney's sudden hospitalization means he won't crew for me today in the regatta." Howard Jackson spoke in a gruff, matter-of-fact voice as if the race were the really important thing.

"I suppose not." She smiled ruefully. "Can you imagine anything more unromantic than a bridegroom agreeing to crew for his father-in-law on the first day of his marriage? I should have refused to marry him for that reason alone!"

"I don't know why you didn't!" her father quipped. "It would have saved us all a great deal of trouble."

"Yes, I know," she said softly, guiltily.

"There . . . there . . . I was only kidding. The important thing is that you're out of it in time."

"I . . . I caused a disaster. All the money . . ."

"Disaster! Hardly! I know it all seems momentous right now, Kitten. And your mother did work herself up into quite a state." His fingers were parting her thick straight hair. "But life goes on. When you're as old as I am, you'll find out sometimes the crisis that seems to spell disaster is really a blessing in disguise. And sometimes we learn more from our mistakes than we ever would if we did everything right."

"I can't see how last night was a blessing when it could have so easily been avoided if I'd . . ."

"Well, you're not Mrs. Rodney Starr for one thing." He arose fingering his watch, his mind on the race once more. "The start's at ten. I came here to ask you to go with me. Your mother's down with one of her headaches. Last night was too much for her. Kitten, why don't you get dressed and come with me? Come on. I really need you. That brash young skipper of *Wild Lady* is going to give me a run for my money on this one. If I don't beat him today, he'll be the first in the series."

"*Wild Lady*." The name pulsated in her brain. It was the nickname Ted had called her five years ago . . . before Rodney . . . Here she was thinking of *him* again. And again she pushed the unhappy memory from her mind.

Her father was at the door, anxious suddenly to be gone. "Well, you coming?"

"No! I couldn't possibly face all those people down there."

"Kitten, what is it you think you have to live down? They gave a few parties for you and had fun doing it. Real friends want what's best for you, and they'll accept what happened without passing judgment. Besides we can return all the gifts. And if a few people are critical of you—I wouldn't care too much what they think because they will have proved they're not genuine friends anyway."

"I can't help it. I feel so guilty to have caused everyone so much trouble when I should have known all along I wasn't doing the right thing."

"Suit yourself!" He glanced down at his watch impatiently. He gave her one last look before he opened the door. Then she heard the door slam, the faint, rapid padding of his boat shoes as he descended the stairs, and later the distant purr of his car in the drive.

Kit sat up amidst the tangle of sheets and regretted for an instant her decision to stay behind. She felt lonely now that he was gone. At least the excitement of the race would have gotten her mind off everything for a while. Still, if she'd gone, she would have had to face everyone. And she wasn't ready.

She was rising from the bed. Once more her eyes drifted out the doors that opened onto her balcony to the grounds and she saw the pool. She would go for a swim . . . and a sunbath . . . a long languid sunbath that would bake away all her miseries. She pulled on her tan bikini—it exactly matched the color of her olive skin. She stepped into her floor-length, see-through lace cover-up so that she was covered from neck to ankle in cream-colored froth and because of her flesh-toned swim suit, it seemed as though she were nude beneath it.

She grabbed a velour bathsheet from her bathroom and as she did, she glanced into the mirror at her face.

The delicate oval was undeniably lovely. Soft brows slanted above large, thickly fringed dark eyes, eyes so dark they appeared almost black. Her nose was straight and delicately boned, her lips full and temptingly soft.

She dabbed at her face with a wet washcloth. Then she brushed her raven-black hair until it shone like silk. As she did she heard the buzz of the doorbell downstairs.

Ignoring the buzz—insistent now—she ran the brush through her shoulder-length hair one last time and put on some lipstick. Again she heard the buzz. She remembered her mother's headache. It was Sunday, the maid Maria's day off. Kit decided to answer the door on her way to the pool.

The buzz was a continual blare throughout the house as she descended the spiral stairs and crossed the gleaming stretch of saltillo tile to stop before the ornate black curve of wrought-iron gates that led to the foyer.

"For heaven's sake!" She felt unusually irritable as the sound persisted and she struggled with the gate. "Whoever's out there must be leaning on the doorbell!"

At last she managed to open the gate, and her bare feet were sinking into the thick pile of the Oriental throw rug in front of the door. All was silence as she peered through the peep hole. No one was there.

She opened the door and looked out. Still no one. Nothing to greet her but the balmy warmth of the new day, the first day of summer, pouring through the half-opened door.

Cautiously she stepped out of the house, and in the distance where the drive curved, she saw a yellow van with bold black lettering on it spelling out, "Bradley's Rental Center."

Bradley! The name should have sounded some sort of alarm, but because she was intent on telling off whomever had been ringing the bell, it didn't.

The doors at the back of the van were open, and she saw beneath them thrust widely apart two darkly tanned, muscled legs that wore ragged boat shoes. The man who belonged to those legs and shoes was rummaging furiously through the van.

She thought of her mother's headache, and the violent pain noise could cause her. Briskly Kit walked in the direction of the van. She'd tell him a thing or two—about standing on a doorbell at eight o'clock on a Sunday morning with her mother ill with a migraine.

The man was still hidden from her view by the door of his truck when she began imperiously, "Is there something I can do for you?"

From the depths of the van she heard a deep, masculine voice that sounded vaguely familiar. "I was stopping off on my way down to my boat to check on that tent y'all rented. Want to check the tension on the poles . . . the tie downs . . . make sure it's secure for the day. The weather forecast said the wind's building."

She cut him off. "Well, next time when you come to the house you should use the servants' entrance around back instead of the front door."

As if in response to her words something dropped with a resounding clatter inside the van, and the man swore under his breath.

She continued. "My mother's ill this morning

16

. . . and I didn't appreciate the way you kept buzz-ing."

A large brown hand gripping the door of the van came slowly into view. And then the man stepped back from the van and out of its shadow—into the brilliant sunlight.

"Kit! Thought I might catch a glimpse of the—how did the paper put it . . . the stranded bride—when I came by this morning."

Her mind registered first the sarcasm and then the anger in his voice.

Kit's fingers—trembling—were at her lips. Her face had paled to the color of cream lace at her throat. She took a faltering step backwards. It couldn't be! It couldn't be! But it was! *It was he!* Ted Bradley!

He towered over her—all arrogant six feet, four inches of him. He was older, of course, and a little heavier than he'd been—more muscular, more power-ful. There were lines at the corners of his lips and beneath his cobalt blue eyes and between his dark brows that hadn't been there five years ago. His skin was bronzed, his auburn hair streaked gold from the sun. He was as handsome as always—even more handsome than she remembered.

Just looking at him—and she was aching all over.

She saw that he was dressed to sail, but unlike her father he wore cut-off jeans and a blue T-shirt with the name of his boat, *Wild Lady,* lettered across it in white.

Things her father had said were coming back to her. The rental outfit was owned by a "brash young upstart that wouldn't give an inch." Her father was tied for first place with the "brash young skipper of *Wild Lady.*" She should have known! Why hadn't she guessed?

Brash! In certain moods the word perfectly fitted the

Ted Bradley she remembered. And she thought, "He's in such a mood now."

His mouth was curling in contempt as he stared down at her. She'd ordered him to the servants' entrance. Oh, why had she done that? He'd always had such a complex about money anyway. Her father's money had intimidated him right from the first. Lines between his eyes deepened as his brows drew together. His eyes were fastened on her face for one long shattering moment, and it seemed to Kit that Time stopped. Everything—Rodney, the horror of the wedding that hadn't been, what other people thought—no longer mattered.

She watched Ted draw a deep breath as if he sought to curb whatever emotion was surging through him. He balled his hands into fists and jammed them into the pockets of his cut-offs.

Then his eyes slid from her face down her throat, over her slim body tantalizingly veiled by the lace the wind was swirling around her. Once more he lifted his gaze to hers, and for an instant she thought she saw hurt in his dark-blue eyes. Then he smiled—insolently.

"So . . . I'm still not good enough to come to your front door," he said softly.

"Ted, I didn't know, I didn't mean . . ."

"Oh, but you did. Your kind doesn't have to know or mean. What you said is all part of the lifestyle you take for granted. Your kind walks through front doors while mine walks through . . . servants' entrances. . . . Maybe I should thank you. You've given me the very thing I needed this morning: that extra ounce of determination to beat your dad, to show him this race is one thing money can't buy."

For an instant she felt hurt. Then she was bristling. As usual he'd taken the upper hand, and what had she done really? Nothing but utter an off-hand remark about the back entrance, the servants' entrance. How could she have known it was he in the truck? She bit her lips.

"I see you still haven't lost your poor-boy chip on the shoulder."

As soon as the words were out of her mouth she knew they were a mistake. He was advancing upon her and seizing her by the wrist, and as always just the touch of him was excitement. She was shivering violently as if it were suddenly cold, and it was still warm. And she'd told herself these past five years she hated him! She tried to twist out of his grasp, but he was too strong. He pulled her to him as if her strength were nothing and gave her a long, searching look.

"When you walked out on me for Rodney, you taught me once and for all the finer distinctions of class. Rich girls don't marry poor boys no matter how attracted they are to them. They might enjoy a fling and a little ardent lovemaking with *them,* but they don't make it a permanent arrangement."

His words stung as he'd intended them to. Half-formed thoughts were whirling in her head. A fling . . . a little ardent lovemaking with *them* . . . as if there'd been many men in her life. When there had only been one man and one night . . . with him. And she'd foolishly thought that he'd cared something for her. She'd been old fashioned and believed such feelings led to marriage. She'd made a commitment to him . . . before marriage, and he'd tried to take advantage of her. She'd been one in a series of many conquests to him . . . doubtless!

Left him for Rodney? As if she'd wanted to leave him! He made her sound so cheap!

The hurt went deep, and angry words rushed to her

lips to cover it. But before she could speak he lowered his mouth to hers and kissed her ruthlessly. She struggled wildly, but to no purpose. He released her wrist, and his arms circled her waist. He pressed the softness of her body so that it tightly fitted his—his that was lean and hard and powerful.

Suddenly her anger was draining away, and the old, familiar weakening was possessing her. She felt again that old sense of passionate joyful belonging only to him. A strange warmth, an exquisite bliss was filling her. She forgot the old hurt. There was only this moment . . . now. . . . Something deep within her— some inner core of happiness that she hadn't even remembered was there—was reawakening for the first time in five years. As always the feel of him was delight and vulnerability and turbulent emotion.

Ted was back in her life, and when he held her it was as if he'd never gone. It was as if there'd never been the gulf of empty years.

Her fingers were in his hair, parting the thick auburn waves. He had always known exactly how to kiss her and where to kiss her that would most arouse her. His lips traveled a leisurely, searing path from her mouth down her cheek to her earlobe. It seemed to her that her blood became hot waves of liquid fire coursing through her arteries. She felt weak—as if she couldn't stand without his support, and she clung to him. He pressed her the more tightly to him with a groan.

She was returning his kisses hungrily. It had been so long. So . . . so long since she'd felt like this. Five years. . . . His touch was madness . . . sweet madness. If only . . . only he would hold her forever. . . .

She felt him stiffen before he pushed her roughly away.

He took a deep, long breath, "And if I've still got

my poor-boy complex, you haven't changed much either. You're still the hot little tease I called Wild Lady."

"How dare you!"

His eyes were traveling lazily from her face downward, and she grew warm all over. "Yes, I dare! What do you expect? You come out here wearing that lacey thing with nothing under it."

"For your information," she said, "I was on my way to the pool when you started ringing the doorbell. I'm wearing a bathing suit under this!"

"Well, you sure can't tell it from here," he said thickly. His eyes were on her face again, on her lips. He turned abruptly from her and strode back to the van and rummaged through it once more.

She knew that she should go, but for some reason she couldn't. Ted Bradley was back in her life—if only for this instant, and in spite of and perhaps because of their long separation, her feelings were more powerful for him than they had ever been.

He emerged from the back of the van once more, a tool kit in his left hand. Her eyes riveted to the gold wedding band that gleamed from the ring finger of that hand.

So . . . he was still married to Letitia. She remembered he'd had a child.

"You're still here?" Quizzical dark brows slanted upward.

"I thought I'd walk with you on my way to the pool . . . through the house," she said weakly.

"I can see I'm coming up in the world," was his sarcastic retort.

"Ted. . . . Please. . . ." She placed her hand on his arm. Her eyes pleaded. "I'm sorry for what I said earlier." Her voice was shaking with emotion.

He saw her distress. "All right," he said curtly, pulling his arm away. "You're forgiven."

She could not stop herself from thinking that he had been back in her life all of ten minutes and their relationship was exactly as it had been. He had done everything that had caused the harsh feelings between them, yet she was apologizing to him.

He was staring deeply into her eyes as if to read her mind and her heart. He looked puzzled suddenly, perplexed. She looked away.

The tool box was clatter on concrete as he set it down and folded her once more into his arms.

"Kit, Kit . . . what is happening to us? It's almost as if you never left . . ." His lips were in her hair.

Even as she felt her body responding to his touch, she was remembering he had a wife and a child. She had to stop him.

"Aren't you forgetting . . . your wife?"

Slowly he pushed her from him. "My wife is dead," he said flatly. "Two years ago she was killed in a car accident. And now I'll find my own way to the pool . . . through the servants' entrance . . . if you don't mind." There was no sarcasm in his voice, only pain.

It was obvious he was not over his wife's death. In the face of his grief, she could think of nothing to say.

He swung around on his heels and left her staring open-mouthed after him as he disappeared around the curve in the drive.

Chapter Two

From the height of her balcony Kit watched Ted as he carefully checked each pole and each tie-down of the tent. The languid, easy grace of his great body fascinated her. He strained against a rope and she watched the pull of brown muscles in his arms. She could see he took his work seriously. His checking of the tent was not a casual observation from some faraway, stand-off position.

Kit had returned to her room because she'd sensed Ted's need to get away from her. Suddenly, watching him, she determined to go down to the pool. This was her home after all! She had a perfect right. . . . She raced from her room, down the stairs, and stopped only when she reached the expanse of sliding glass doors that opened from the den onto the patio and pool area. She caught her breath and slid one of the doors open.

Slowly, as though in a dream, she moved to the edge of the pool and laid her wine-colored bathsheet down lengthwise.

She unhooked the lacy cover-up where it fastened at the neck, and let it fall from her body into a puddle of cream froth circling her feet. The swim suit she wore was like an outer skin of olive silk that did nothing to hide her luscious curves. Out of the corner of her eye, she saw Ted stop what he was doing and look at her, his eyes traveling slowly down from the soft swell of full breasts, to her narrow waist, her well-turned hips, and graceful thighs. . . . He turned away quickly, too quickly, but not before her own pulse was hammering wildly.

She saw the darkening flush of his cheeks; she saw his frown, his attempted nonchalance as he turned his attention once more to his tent. And she smiled. He was pulling fiercely on a rope as she stepped over the cover-up and picked it up. Suddenly the pole he was working on fell, and a section of tent sagged.

"Need some help?" she called gaily.

Gruffly: "No!"

She lay down upon the soft velour and watched his struggles with the tent pole. She could feel the warmth of the tile through her towel, and already the sun was baking on her back.

Once more he had the pole in place and the tie-down taut. Deliberately ignoring her, he moved to the next pole and checked it.

She lay there by the pool trying to fit the pieces together. She should've guessed that Ted Bradley was the owner of the rental outfit and the skipper of *Wild Lady*. She'd known he'd returned to Corpus shortly after he'd married. But it had all happened such a long time ago, and she'd deliberately avoided trying to find out what happened to him—for just the thought of him had meant pain.

Still, she'd heard her father mention his boat, *Wild Lady*. At the time the name had rung a bell. But she hadn't thought . . .

Wild Lady. . . . Once long ago Ted had called her that . . . many times . . . usually after he'd held her in his arms, sensing her leaping response. She'd thought it had been his special name for her. Now she wondered. Had he named his boat after her? Or, was it merely his turn of phrase? Something he called all his girlfriends?

The past came back in a sweeping rush. The night of that storm . . . the night she'd almost made love to him in that tiny efficiency apartment he'd been renting off 24th Street in Austin. The night she'd found out what kind of man he really was.

Afterward Kit had supposed such nights of love meant little to him. She had attempted to console herself with Rodney's offer of friendship.

Kit looked up and saw that Ted was staring at her once more. He moved toward her.

"Well, it shouldn't blow away . . . today anyway," he said in his most businesslike voice.

"I wish it would . . . blow away . . . out of my sight. It reminds me of . . ."

"Always the careless, rich girl out of tune with the harsher realities of Life. That tent cost me a lot of money, and it isn't insured."

Had it always been this easy to get angry at him? "I didn't mean . . ." she faltered.

"You never mean . . . do you? But you've reminded me. What happened last night?"

"Read the paper!" she snapped. "Page sixteen!"

"I already have, and if you ask me, that was the luckiest night of your life!"

"I didn't ask you!"

"No, you didn't! But just to show you my heart's in the right place, I'll wish you luck in snagging old Rodney."

"I don't want your good wishes!"

"Well, you have them just the same. After all, I have a personal interest in your success. Who knows, maybe you'll rent the tent from me again!"

"Not on your life!"

He was punching a button on his quartz watch and reading the time. "I can always hope, can't I? But I've gotta get going. The start's at ten, and if I leave right now I'll just make the skippers' meeting. I've gotta show your dad a thing or two about sailing. Remember?"

When he'd gone, Kit flew to her room and pulled a T-shirt and a pair of shorts over her bathing suit. She grabbed her boat shoes and dashed down the stairs to the garage.

She was sinking into the baby-blue leather of her bucket seat and fumbling with the keys in the ignition.

Radials were hugging asphalt and squealing as the Porsche sped out onto the boulevard that followed the curve of the bay from her home to the yacht club.

She eyed the sparkling waters to her right with misgiving. It was still early in the morning, and already the wind was whipping the waves so that white froth laced their crests. A horn sounded impatiently behind her and she turned her attention once more to the road.

So . . . she'd changed her mind. She would crew for her father this morning. And why not? The race was exactly what she needed to get her mind off . . . off . . . things. . . .

Who cared what people thought?

The parking lot near the yacht club was full so Kit had to park near the shrimp boats. As she swung the long, brown curves of her legs out of the car, three shrimpers ceased their work at their nets and leered. When she stepped from her car, they whistled madly. Flushing, she avoided their gaze, finished locking her car, and walked slowly toward the club.

Open masculine admiration from strangers embarrassed her. She'd only exulted in admiration like that from one man—Ted. For some reason she'd always found the intent way his gaze followed her pleasurable and exciting. Rodney had never looked at her like that. The shrimpers called after her in Spanish, but she ignored them and quickened her steps.

Noiselessly she entered the bar of the club, which was a bustle of confusion. The skippers' meeting had just been concluded, and the skippers and their crew members were grabbing Styrofoam cups filled with coffee to take with them to their boats where they would finish last-minute rigging.

At first no one noticed Kit, and she viewed the sea of familiar faces uneasily. Many of them had been guests last night, witnesses to the fiasco of her supposed "wedding."

"Hey, Bradley," Marc Clay called. "Did you hear Jackson bought a new heavy-air spinnaker just to help him on the downwind leg of the race?"

At the mention of her father's name, Kit noted his conspicuous absence. Then she looked beyond, through the floor-to-ceiling sheets of glass that formed two walls of the bar, and saw the black hull of *Kitten*, her father's boat, still tied at her dock and her father and her brother, Steve, packing the spinnaker bag. Yards of blowing, ballooning black and yellow silk-like cloth—the new spinnaker—were spilling from the bag. The two men were scrambling to control it.

Then she heard Ted's voice, brash and arrogant. "Hell, Jackson can buy all the sails he wants, but I intend to show him sails and money don't win races. Skippers do!"

Her eyes shifted from *Kitten* to him. He was standing in one corner of the room, one of his great arms gripping the polished brass railing of the staircase that spiraled upward to the dining room. The other arm rested negligently upon the shoulder of a darkly beautiful woman who was wearing a T-shirt like his. *His* wife! But . . . she was dead! Still, the resemblance was uncanny! Kit had seen Letitia once, five years ago, and she'd never forgotten her dark, almost exotic beauty.

Suddenly Kit was furious. How dare he say such a thing about her father?

Kit's heart was pounding rabbit-fast when she heard her voice, a curious choking sound, cry out as if it had a mind of its own. "Mr. Bradley, I think that remark was rude and uncalled for. My father was merely buying a sail he needed for his boat. I don't think he feels his money can buy races!" She broke off. For one terrible moment she thought she'd strangle on her anger.

Then Ted's eyes were on her; and they were alight with sardonic interest. His great arm fell from the dark girl's shoulder. He smiled broadly.

The crowd hushed and shifted its attention to her. There was a faint buzz in one corner near her, and Kit as did everyone else in the room heard the unmistakable, the terribly cruel words, "You wouldn't think she'd have enough nerve to come here . . . after last night. . . ." Then the woman, aware the room had suddenly gone silent, hushed.

Kit went red with embarrassment. Why? Why had she called attention to herself? Last night—when she'd stood before these very people—came back in a sickening flash. She'd caused them all such trouble, and she'd made a fool of herself as well.

Then she saw Ted moving toward her. She was dizzy suddenly, and just as she thought she'd faint, his hand was supporting her elbow.

His eyes held hers for a long moment, and the dizzy feeling intensified.

His fingers moved beneath her elbow—warm and electric. Would it always be like this? He had only to touch her, to look at her, and the world would spin. She pushed the disturbing possibility from her mind.

Was his an appeal that all women found as irresistible as she did?

He was strikingly handsome, tall and powerfully built. The blue eyes that studied her face were brilliant, magnetic; and she could not look away. His steady, intense gaze was stripping away all the bandages she'd so carefully wrapped around her heart. Suddenly she was aching as if he'd exposed a deep hurt—that uncovered—was as rawly painful as an unhealed wound.

She grew warm all over. He saw too much. He had no right to come back into her life. . . .

She was angry again and frightened because he could so effortlessly arouse all the old feelings. Did she . . . was it possible . . . that she still cared something for him . . . even knowing the kind of man he was.

"No, it isn't possible!" she told herself desperately. What she felt for Ted had to be physical, nothing more.

The wisest course for her to follow would be to avoid him in the future.

She pulled her elbow away from him, noting with satisfaction the quick hardening of his expression. Maybe if he grew angry he would leave. But he didn't. Instead he leaned his great body against the wall behind her and continued to stare down at her.

Her heart was hammering wildly. And only because he was near. Why? Did he attract her because he was different from all that she was used to, different from Rodney and from this roomful of wealthy young men, who skippered the other boats? She viewed their smooth faces, faces unlined by struggle, with distaste. Everything they had had come too easily to them while Ted had fought for everything he possessed.

She admired that in him. His features that were bronzed from work out of doors were rugged. She noted the faint grooves etched between the thick slash of his dark brows. She fought against the desire to reach up and trace the faint lines until they went smooth beneath her fingertips. She noted the long hawklike nose, the square, determined set of his jaw, his bold eyes. She was flushing again as he continued to stare at her in that carelessly reckless yet intense, way of his, smiling insolently, his even straight teeth a flash of white against his swarthy skin. She thought he looked ruthless, almost piratical.

A delicious shiver shook her, and, as if he knew it to be her response to him, his smile widened. She looked quickly away. He laughed as if he had read her mind and seen the battle raging there.

Oh, if she were smart she would run out of the club and away from him at once. Yet she stayed rooted to the spot.

"You couldn't resist the challenge of trying to put

me . . . or keep me . . . as the case may be . . . in my proper place, could you?" he said. Again the wide smile, and the Buccaneer gleam in his eyes. "The real Jackson Wild Lady against . . . her name sake, my *Wild Lady?* Should be an interesting race."

Did he mean he *had* named his boat after her? She looked up at him furious again, but her anger dissolved when she saw his blue eyes were twinkling. If he were a pirate, he was in a mischievous mood. He was still smiling as if the sight of her delighted him, and suddenly, in spite of everything, she was smiling too. He was deliberately baiting her, trying to distract her from the woman's malicious remark that had reminded her of last night. He was being kind—in his own peculiar way. For some reason she was inexplicably happy this was so. For the briefest space of time as he looked at her and she looked at him, it seemed to her they were in a world of their own.

As if in a dream she saw his lips move; she heard the deep resonant tones of his voice, breaking the spell, challenging her once more. "So you're gonna help your dad try to beat me? He told me he'd asked you to crew and you'd refused . . ." He smiled knowingly. "Something . . . that happened this morning after he left . . . must've changed your mind." When she still refused to rise to his bait, he hesitated. "Someday, Kit, I hope we'll be on the same side . . . for a change. . . ." His voice wrapped her with its warmth.

He turned and saw that the dark, exotic beauty across the room was beckoning to him. Smiling, he waved to her.

Then he was leading Kit across the room, and she was acutely aware of his hand lightly touching the back of her waist. Kit knew that heads were turning in their

31

direction, that there was a speculative buzz behind them.

When they reached the young woman Ted said, "Kit, I want you to meet Phyllis Lanier, my sister-in-law." The dark girl with the fiery gray eyes was glaring at her. "She takes care of my little girl, Missy, for me in the afternoons."

The dark girl jerked her head toward Kit and her thick crop of short curls caught the sunlight and gleamed like black fire.

"Well, I'm happy to meet you, Kit." Her gray eyes, stony with dislike, belied her words. "But, Ted, don't you think we'd better go out to the boat . . . now?"

It was obvious to Kit that Phyllis resented her presence.

"Phyllis, why don't you go out and try to rustle up Rick first. We can't leave without him anyway," Ted said.

"But . . . aren't you coming with me?"

"I'll be along in a minute. I want to show Kit *Wild Lady.*"

Phyllis did as he suggested even though she seemed reluctant to leave Kit alone with Ted. For a sister-in-law, she was certainly possessive.

When she was gone Ted turned back to Kit. "Kit, would you like to see *Wild Lady?*" He was taking her hand, and pulling her through the crowd.

Oh, she was a fool to go with him! She should snatch her hand from his and go help her father rig *Kitten.* But when had she ever been sensible about him? She did not snatch her hand away. He led her from the yacht club piers to one of the more undesirable slips— undesirable because it was shallow and the wind and currents brought a veritable floating island of garbage—paper cups, bits of plastic, beer bottles, slicks of grease—to float trapped in the spot where two walls of concrete bulkhead joined together.

"I've been trying to get a better slip for over a year, but they're all taken," he said. "And *Wild Lady* is the only boat with a shallow enough draft to be tied here."

Kit admired the trim lines of *Wild Lady*'s ice-blue, wooden hull. She was a sloop, twenty-six feet long. At the stern the boat's name was a swirl of bold golden script that looked like Ted's handwriting.

He helped her onto the boat, and proudly showed her below. "I made her myself," he was saying. He ran his palm fondly across a piece of decking. "I know every board, every fitting . . ."

"She is very beautiful, Ted," Kit began.

At her words, he smiled. She noticed that the lines around his eyes were no longer there.

He was about to say something. He seemed eager to, and then he caught himself. He seemed angry suddenly at himself for his own enthusiasm. "She's really nothing, I guess, compared to a fancy rig like your dad's boat, *Kitten*. She's homemade, cheap in comparison, and I'm sure she couldn't impress someone like you."

Before she could reply, he was looking beyond her, and leaping from the boat to help Phyllis who was struggling to carry a heavily laden ice chest to the boat.

Phyllis's eyes were on Kit—accusing. "Ted, it's nine-fifteen. Don't you think we'd better get going?"

"Soon as Rick gets here."

"He's right behind me."

A tall pole of a boy with a thatch of red hair appeared. Rick. Slung over his bony shoulder was a sail bag.

Feeling out of place, as if she no longer belonged, Kit tugged on the dock line. Just as she stepped onto the dock, an angry motorist honked his horn at two pedestrians in his way. Startled by the unexpected noise, she slipped, and if Ted hadn't pulled her swiftly into his arms she would have fallen into the water.

He was crushing her head against his chest. She heard the wild beating of his heart; she felt the hard warmth of his body. She regained her balance, and still—for one long wonderful moment—he held her as if he enjoyed the feel of her against him. Then he released her. She felt his eyes on her face, but she did not dare look up for fear that he would see how shaken she was from being in his arms—if only for an instant.

"Getting clumsy in your old age," he mocked softly. "Hope you're not becoming accident prone like your bridegroom Rodney . . ."

Angrily she pushed him from her and ran past him. Behind her she heard his quick burst of laughter, but she never looked back.

She was breathless when she reached *Kitten*, and her father, surprised to see her, looked up from his task of uncoiling the main sheet.

"Steve, help her on board," was her father's command. And to her: "You look as if the Devil himself were at your heels." Then his voice became a bark of orders. "Cast off that port line. And now, cast off the starboard line . . . but hold on to it. Tightly! No . . . let it go!" When she didn't obey instantly: *"Let it go!"* She dropped it into the water. "Fend off! Fend off!" She leaned her weight against a piling so that *Kitten* wouldn't scrape it.

Twenty-seven feet of black fiberglass backed slowly out of her slip. Steve shifted into forward and moved the tiller. Kit sat back on top of the cabin and tried to stop thinking of Ted.

The sea breeze was ruffling her long black hair as she

34

slipped a bright-red triangular scarf over it. She heard the steady clang of the metal rigging against the aluminum mast, the wash of water curling back from the bow as the boat slipped through the waves, the steady chugging of the diesel, and the cry of a gull behind her. All was like music—soothing.

"Bring her up into the wind, Steve. Not through it! There! I'm going to hoist the main sail."

Kit smiled fondly as she watched her brother follow her father's orders. He moved the tiller with a quiet sureness that was characteristic of him. She always marveled at the way Steve and her father got along. Her father turned into Captain Bly on races, but that never ruffled Steve. Together, the two men made an almost unbeatable combination.

She watched Howard Jackson kneeling beneath the mast and pulling with all his strength on the main halyard. The big sail crawled slowly up the mast; the bottom of it unfurled from the boom that was swinging well over Steve's head as he stood up in the cockpit. Within seconds her father had raised the Genoa, an oversized foresail, also.

"With that Genoa up, I can't see a thing," Steve was muttering. He ran his hand through his dark hair in agitation. "Kit, get up to the bow at once—to the pulpit—and keep an eye out for other boats."

From the pulpit: *"Sashay* is under you, but you're all right. Hold your course. Do you see *Butterfly?"*

"Yea . . ."

"Wild Lady" . . . Her voice caught and faded into an inaudible murmur at the sight of Ted sitting terribly close to Phyllis. His expression was intense; he was so engrossed in conversation with his sister-in-law that he failed to wave to Kit as the two boats passed one

another. Unaccountably this omission on his part hurt much more than it should have.

Kit failed to call out another boat's position and her brother, seeing the other yacht in the nick of time, tacked abruptly.

"Kit, what the devil are you thinking about up there?" her brother called in exasperation.

"Sorry . . ."

Brother and sister continued shouting back and forth to one another as Kit sighted other sailboats and called their positions to Steve. Her father was setting out lines, checking fittings, and keeping a sharp watch for the white starting flag which would indicate there were ten minutes remaining before the start.

The flag went up, and Howard Jackson instantly punched the button of his nautical-looking stopwatch. Her father took one look across the starting line and frowned.

"Steve, I think we better make a run across that line."

"Tacking . . ." Steve called.

Uneasily Kit watched the foredeck become white flapping chaos as the Genoa swept across it. Then once more the big sail was trimmed again, and the boat was heeling and moving forward on the opposite tack. She wished they could change the Genoa for the smaller working jib sail. But she knew better than to question her father's judgment. Instead she hung onto the chrome bars of the pulpit for dear life.

Howard Jackson was closely studying the starting line, that invisible line that stretched across the water between a buoy and the committee boat. "Looks like the buoy near the jetty is the favored end of the line, and the port tack will be the favored tack. Which means . . . that if we cross high up on that end of the

line on port tack we won't have right-of-way. There
won't be any forgiveness for error."

Fifty boats! It wasn't going to be easy to be in the
right spot when that gun went off. *Kitten* would be on a
port tack with no right-of-way. If anyone made a
mistake or refused to give right-of-way . . . there could
be a collision . . .

Chapter Three

A burst of fluttering blue—the exact color of Ted's eyes—was hoisted from the committee boat to replace the white, ten-minute flag. Only five minutes remained until the start. Unsmilingly, Kit watched the many boats that were now sailing—all in different directions, seemingly all on different courses. She knew, however, that each skipper was carefully timing himself, trying to figure the wind, and his boat's speed so that he could cross the starting line the precise moment the red flag went up and the gun sounded.

Too many boats—to be at the same place at the same time!

Her father was at the tiller.

"Two and a half minutes 'til the start. We've gotta tack in fifteen seconds."

"*Force 12* is coming up fast," Kit called from the pulpit.

"I see her. We've got room."

Steve was removing the thick coil of Genoa sheet from the chrome-plated winch in preparation for the tack.

"Tacking—now!"

The bow of the boat turned, the air went out of the foresail, and Steve released the sheet. Everything seemed to happen at once.

The foresail crackled like stiff paper and Steve began trimming it on the starboard winch. The main sail caught the wind, and the boom jerked across the cockpit. *Kitten* was heeling again and moving fast.

Kitten heeled at an even more precarious angle as Steve continued to winch the big sail in, and Kit tightened her grip on the metal bars of the pulpit. For some reason she felt unusually nervous. Then she saw the ice blue hull of *Wild Lady* coming up fast. *Wild Lady* was still on a starboard tack. Apparently Ted intended to tack at the last minute. When he did tack he would be almost in the exact position as her father. It was incredible the way the best skippers ended up at the same place at the crucial moments.

She observed Ted at the helm, his auburn hair ruffling in the wind, his face ruthless and determined, determined to win at any cost—just as her father was. This time he saw her. For a brief moment his dark face lit with joy. He waved to her jauntily, and she— delighted, too delighted—returned his wave.

Suddenly she heard it. A whir at first, followed by a metallic snap. Her father's voice was a roar in the cockpit. "The Genoa track's pulling out!" Kit watched with horror as the ribbon of stainless track pulled loose from the deck.

Her father was shouting. "Steve! Keep that Genoa sheet on the winch! Kit, get back in the cockpit!"

As Kit crawled across the high side of the deck to the cockpit, a heavy gust knocked *Kitten* over and her low side went under. The winch Steve was working on was completely under water. Slowly the boat righted herself.

Her brother cursed low beneath his breath. "Blast! The winch is fouled! I can't get the sail in!" Louder: "Dad, she's fouled!"

The winch with the layers of overlapping rope looked like a giant silver spool of tangled thread.

Kit saw the big sail luffing, spilling air. The sail was flapping and making so much noise she could scarcely hear anything else.

"Kit, take the helm!" her father ordered.

"But, Daddy, I . . . I haven't sailed in years. I . . ." There was no crossing her father when he was determined.

Her father was yelling. "Hold her up . . . high! Higher!" He grabbed the tiller and pushed it where he wanted it. "There! Keep her heading for that water tower. I've gotta get below! Gotta get the tool kit so I can cut that snarl of sheet off the winch."

Kit fought to point the boat toward the water tower squatting like a giant orange spider on the horizon. Her father disappeared into the cabin and reemerged almost at once with his tool kit.

Without the foresail trimmed in tightly, the boat could not point where her father wanted it to. Kit couldn't see around the big foresail either, and she knew sailboats were everywhere—sailboats on different courses, sailboats she couldn't see.

Steve was intent upon trying to unfoul the winch. Suddenly Kit heard—above the noise of the sail and too-near—the ominous, "Starboard tack! Right-of-way!" Louder: *"Kitten,* give us right-of-way!"

Her father would have reacted with reflex, split-second timing, and tacked, and thereby, avoided the collision. But Kit was sailing, and she was exhausted from her sleepless night. She moved more slowly, too slowly.

As if in a dream, she heard the other skipper's voice—Ted's much louder now, shouting to his crew, "Tack! Tack! Now! *Kitten*'s not . . ."

His orders became a blur of sound as a sudden gust of air howled, and *Kitten* slammed to a stand-still. Water was again rushing into the cockpit.

Kit heard the terrible sound of wood splintering— *Wild Lady*'s hull breaking as *Kitten*'s bow sliced through it. Another gust screamed, and Kit dropped the tiller. Her father was scrambling to free the main sheet so the main sail would no longer fill with wind and propel the boat forward. Steve was grabbing for the knife in the toolkit so he could cut the Genoa loose and collapse that sail.

Kit froze. This couldn't be happening! It couldn't!

Another gust swept across the cockpit and knocked *Kitten* over, and Kit lost her footing and plunged toward the low side into the water.

When she surfaced, she heard someone screaming her name. Then she saw bearing down on her four tons of white fiberglass! *Butterfly!* And Kris, the skipper of *Butterfly*, did not see her. He was looking instead at *Wild Lady*.

Then suddenly, Ted was in the water with her, grabbing her into his great arms, pushing her out of the way. She heard his words: "Take a deep breath . . ."

And then she heard no more. Dark waters were curling over her face as he pushed her beneath the waves and held her there. She struggled but to no

41

purpose. He held her with the weight of his body on hers.

When she thought she'd surely drown, when she thought she must open her mouth and breathe water, his body jolted hard against hers and pressed her even deeper into the water. He slackened his grip on her arms. Again she struggled and this time he released her. She fought her way to the surface.

She opened her eyes—burning with salt water—and saw the stern of *Butterfly* near, but moving away. Kris had seen them and tacked. Thank heavens!

Kit gasped for breath, sputtering. Once, and then again. Ted was in the water beside her, and she was relieved to see that he was also all right.

"You okay?" Ted asked. Once more she was sputtering. "Don't try to talk," he said. "Here . . . hold onto this cushion." He pushed the strap handles of a floating white square into her fingers. She saw the black print that read *"Butterfly"* stenciled onto the top of the cushion. She saw several other cushions, similarly marked in the water nearby. Kris must have tossed them from his boat as he'd passed. Then Kit noticed that Ted's face, usually so dark, was nearly as white as the cushions. She saw the wine-red stains in the water circling him, the dark smears on his blue T-shirt. She remembered how his body jolted hard against hers when he'd held her under. Suddenly she understood. Hě'd been hit by *Butterfly!* And *Butterfly* was sailing away as if nothing had happened.

Ted had been hit, and he'd shielded her from the impact of that blow with his body. He'd risked his life to save her. If he'd been hit on the head, he could've been . . .

"Ted, are you . . ."

He cut her off. "Your dad's got his sails down at last. He's going to pick us up. Hang onto that cushion. I'm not up to any more heroics today on your account."

She heard the purr of *Kitten*'s diesel and saw Steve lowering the aluminum ladder over the stern.

She placed her foot on the bottom rung, and Steve was reaching over the side to help her. At last she stood—bedraggled, dripping and shivering—in the cockpit. Ted was still in the water, and she leaned down to tell him to board.

"Ted . . ."

For a moment she thought he did not hear her. Then she saw that he was looking past *Kitten* to *Wild Lady*. There was a deathly stillness to his features. At last he tore his eyes from *Wild Lady*, from her badly damaged hull, from the squirts of water Phyllis was pumping out of the cabin, from Rick struggling to fit the small outboard motor into place.

Kit realized in that instant the magnitude of what she had done to him. *Wild Lady* was more to Ted than just a boat. He hadn't ordered her from a boat dealer. He hadn't simply written a check. He'd built her himself afternoons after work. It must've taken him months. He'd put part of himself into her—she was a work of love. And she, Kit, had destroyed *Wild Lady*.

Ted grabbed the ladder with his left hand and— slowly, carefully—pulled himself out of the water and into the cockpit.

"Well, so this is what it's like in the enemy camp," he said, attempting lightness. "High style." His expression darkened as his eyes went again to *Wild Lady*. "I should be over there—with them—helping. Rick still hasn't gotten that motor started."

Kit saw that Ted's right arm dangled crookedly, that

43

his right shoulder was dark with blood stains. He was now ashen from the strain of pulling himself into the boat.

"They'll have to manage," she said gently. "You're in no condition to do anything but sit down."

His hard gaze drifted over her. She was suddenly aware that her soaking T-shirt clung to her curves. "And who should I thank for that, Miss?" he asked brutally.

Her eyes were burning again, this time from tears not salt water. She was remembering his eagerness, his pride when he'd showed her *Wild Lady*. And she'd wrecked *Wild Lady!* And his arm. . . . It looked broken. That was her fault too. It was obvious although he was trying to conceal it that he was in pain. Why did she always—always—do everything wrong where he was concerned?

His eyes—bold blue and intense with emotion—continued to gaze down at her. His expression was hard, and she wouldn't blame him if he hated her for what she had done. Abruptly he turned away. Shaking with cold, she sat down.

"Sorry about all this, Bradley," her father said. "Our Genoa track pulled out and the winch fouled. I had to give the helm to Kit. She was in no condition after . . . last. . . . Well, anyway, I was shorthanded this morning."

Kit sensed her father's deep embarrassment that his boat, his daughter, and therefore, *he* was responsible for the accident. Her father was a perfectionist in everything.

"Daddy, I . . ." A violent shiver—almost a seizure—shook her as a blast of wind whipped across the cockpit. "I'm sorry . . . I'm sorry . . ." Her teeth were chattering so much she couldn't speak.

"You're freezing, Kitten," her father said. "Steve, get some blankets from below. I'm sure Bradley could use one too. Kitten, you don't need to apologize. I needed you to crew, and we might've been in worse shape without you. Bradley, the boy's got your motor started, but I think we ought to follow *Wild Lady* in."

"Thank you, sir."

Steve reemerged from the cabin. "I couldn't find but one blanket."

"Give it to Kit," Ted said.

Steve wrapped Kit in king-sized yellow wool. Ted sat down beside her, and she saw the goosebumps dimpling his tanned arms. He was cold, but she realized he would never admit it.

"Ted, why don't you put part of this blanket around you too? You're as cold as I am."

"I'm okay," he replied in clipped tones.

It was painfully clear he didn't want any contact with her.

"Kitten's right," her father insisted, "It's the only practical solution. Even though it's summer it's always colder on the water, especially when you're wet."

Ted stood up so that Steve could spread the blanket out all the way, and then he sat down once more—this time closer to Kit—much closer. Steve—careful of Ted's injured shoulder—draped the rest of the blanket over his back.

Kit was still shivering violently. Ted sat stiffly beside her, making no move to touch her.

In spite of the circumstances she felt a strange sense of elation that he was near her. She fancied the blanket wrapped them like a cocoon in a private, secret world of their own. His nearness brought back the past. Steve, her father, the scent of salt in the air, the green sparkle of sunlight on waves mingled and blurred.

Five years ago it had felt like this. Ted had only to come into a room, to hold her hand, and he became her world. Once, nothing . . . no one had mattered to her except him. And then . . . the aching emptiness when she'd broken up with him.

She fought against the old, powerful feeling. He cared nothing for her, Kit, now . . . nor did she care . . . really . . . about him. She didn't! She couldn't! Not now—knowing what kind of man he was. What she was feeling was physical. It was like chemistry—two chemicals exploding when they touched. Was that love?

With difficulty she reminded herself that Ted was no longer part of her life. Somehow she would have to conquer her treacherous feelings for Ted . . . however powerful they were.

Salt spray showered them and brought her attention back to the present . . . to the disaster she'd caused. Howard Jackson was steering *Kitten* so that she followed *Wild Lady* as she limped to her slip. They were moving at a snail's pace, and it would be quite some time before they reached the dock.

"Looks like there's quite a bit of damage, expensive damage, to her hull, Bradley. And your arm will require medical attetnion as well." Howard Jackson hesitated as if he didn't quite know how to phrase his next words. "I'd like to pay for your medical bills and for the repairs," he began slowly.

She felt Ted's body stiffen. His fingers gripped her arm.

"That won't be necessary," he said curtly.

"Still, I feel responsible. If it weren't . . ."

Again Ted's fingers tightened.

"Jackson, I like to think *Wild Lady* is one thing even

your money can't buy. She's mine. All mine. . . . I can and I will get her repaired without your help."

There was no mistaking the determination in Ted's voice. It was as if he'd interpreted Howard's offer to help as a threat to his independence rather than as an offer made out of friendship to help.

Kit held her breath. Her father couldn't possibly understand Ted's refusal to accept his help for he knew nothing of her past relationship with him. He would think Ted rude, and he would be furious.

Oh, why did Ted have to have such a complex about her father's money?

Kitten pitched on a power boat and the tension went out of Ted's grip. He caught his breath and doubled slightly as if he were in pain. But he said nothing.

A long uneasy silence had fallen. Her father, his right hand mechanically guiding the tiller, stared grimly ahead. Kit knew he must be seething with anger and she was dreading the moment when he would explode with some angry retort. She tensed for the probable violent reaction from her father. But the eruption did not come.

Instead she heard her father begin blandly as if he'd carefully considered his answer, "I understand how you feel . . . perfectly. I would have felt the same way myself once."

Kitten pitched again, and this time Ted winced. Kit saw him whiten and press his lips tightly together.

"But here," her father continued, "I can see that arm is painful. At least let me offer you a shot of brandy. I'll get it myself. Steve, take the tiller."

Howard Jackson descended into the cabin and returned almost at once with a column of cellophane-bagged, Styrofoam cups and a bottle of brandy—the finest import money could buy. When he'd poured the brandy into a cup, he offered it to Ted.

Ted released Kit and moved his arm beneath the blanket. He took the cup and lifted it to his lips. "It is excellent . . . naturally," he said. "The best. I feel better already. . . ." He drained the cup.

Howard was pouring him another cupful.

Ted sipped the second cup more slowly. The brandy seemed to have an instant mellowing effect on his mood.

"Jackson, perhaps there is a way you could help me get *Wild Lady* back in shape. Kris told me you're an ace when it comes to tuning a mast. When I get the hull repaired, do you think you could give me a hand with the mast?"

"I'd be glad to, of course," her father answered emphatically. He was clearly pleased Ted had requested his help.

The two men began to discuss the technical aspects of sailing. Her father was asking Ted's advice about his broken Genoa track, and Ted was telling him exactly how he would repair it if it were his. Kit listened to them in amazement. They were enjoying one another's company. It seemed almost as though they were old friends.

After a while they fell silent. Steve had gone to the bow with the boat hook to prepare to dock the boat. Howard Jackson manuevered *Kitten* so that she was as close as possible to the dock so that Ted could easily get off the boat.

Ted was slowly pulling himself to his feet. "Kit . . ." She looked up. His voice was deep, husky. He reached down and brushed a stray tendril of her hair back from her cheek and then drew his hand quickly away as though he touched fire. Slowly he said, "It was almost worth wrecking *Wild Lady* to . . ." She was listening breathlessly, but he did not finish.

Phyllis's voice—shrill with alarm—interrupted him, and he looked up.

"Ted! You've been hurt! Your shirt's all bloody! Your arm! We've got to get you to a hospital!" She glared at Kit accusingly. "This is *your* fault!"

"Phyllis!" Ted's voice was sharp with reproach and the girl became silent at once. More gently: "I know you're concerned, Phyllis, but what happened was an accident. Blaming Kit won't help." He stepped from the boat. Phyllis's arms went around him possessively. "Thanks, Phyllis, for getting *Wild Lady* back to her dock."

"Bradley . . ." Her father called briskly, looking up from securing a dock line, "I'd like to invite you over to dinner if you're up to it. Say Wednesday night. And bring Phyllis too. We can discuss that mast of yours."

"We couldn't possibly come," Phyllis began in a rush. "Ted's been seriously injured. *Wild Lady* . . ."

"Nonsense, Phyllis," Ted said in a voice of steel. "I'll give you a call, Jackson, about dinner . . . later tonight. Should know something about this arm by then."

Kit stepped lithely onto the dock. "Ted, if there's anything I can do for you . . ."

His gaze swept over her and in spite of her soaking clothes she felt oddly warm. But he said nothing; it was Phyllis who blurted,

"I think you've done more than enough for one day, don't you?"

"I didn't mean to. I . . ." Kit broke off.

For just an instant Ted's manner softened toward her. "I know you didn't." He made his voice low—just for her. More loudly: "I'm gonna check on *Wild Lady* now. Finally figured out something good about her slip—even at high tide, it's too shallow for her to sink in it. She'll just sit in the mud."

Then he turned, as if talking about *Wild Lady* made him impatient to check on her. He strode abruptly away.

Kit watched him slow his pace because of his injured arm. The sight of him, in pain, heading for his wrecked boat, caught at her heart. She started after him. "I've got to find some way to help him. I've got to!"

Phyllis was racing behind her, catching up to her. "Why don't you help by leaving him alone?" she asked vehemently. "You nearly ruined his life once! When will you realize, all you can ever be to him is trouble?"

Kit stopped. Phyllis was right, of course. She no longer had a place in his life. Circumstances—unpleasant ones—had thrown them briefly together again—that was all. Kit watched—dazed—as the two of them disappeared together behind the out-buildings of the yacht club.

Chapter Four

Kit sped into the curving driveway and braked the Porsche to a standstill before three stories of pretentious white walls and turrets capped with red tile gleaming in the sunlight. She left her car parked in the drive and ran toward the front door.

Had it only been half an hour ago that she'd stood on the dock by *Kitten* and watched Ted walk slowly away from her with Phyllis?

She stepped into the house. All was just as she'd left it. The ballroom still stood in readiness for the reception that had never been. The silver punch bowls and champagne fountains gleamed on the elegantly-skirted banquet tables. The three-tiered wedding cake had not been moved. Columns of crystal plates, napkins, and silverware remained.

She gazed around her—the familiar surroundings seemed . . . different. She had the odd sensation that she was a stranger in her own home. With no regard at all for the upholstery, she sank—still wet from her dunking—into a nearby chair.

She felt lost . . . in a state of shock. Ted had come back into her life and by doing so he'd shaken the structure of her life to the roots of its foundation. Once she'd thought she was over him, and now . . .

How did she feel about him? She honestly didn't know. Everytime he touched her it was like an electric shock to her system. When he'd walked away from her with Phyllis, she, Kit, had felt desolate. She'd thought he must hate her for wrecking *Wild Lady* and breaking his arm.

It didn't make sense to her that his feelings about her should matter. He was a part of her past . . . that was all . . . a painful memory.

The house was funeral-parlor quiet—much too still. What she needed was action—someone to talk to . . . anything . . . to distract her from thinking of Ted. But her father and brother had not returned from the yacht club and her mother was in bed with her headache. She didn't feel up to calling Rodney yet. Rodney—there was another problem. What was she going to do about him?

She sprang from her chair and rushed desperately to her room. She changed from her wet clothes into a hot pink T-shirt and jeans.

Ted . . . Ted. . . . The name seemed to throb in her head. Almost frantically she brushed her black hair into a ponytail and tied a pink scarf around it. Dressed, she returned once more to the ballroom.

She attacked a stack of crystal plates. She would carry them . . . everything to the kitchen. She had to have something to do or she would go mad thinking of . . . Ted.

It didn't matter that tomorrow when her mother had recovered from her migraine she would organize the maids to clean away everything. It was imperative she occupy herself now.

Ted. . . . He had sat so stiffly beside her when they'd shared the blanket. He'd scarcely spoken to her. She paused at what she was doing and her breath caught painfully. It had felt like this five years ago when she'd lost him. Was she going to suffer it all over again? No! She wasn't. She wasn't!

She determined to spend the day putting away all the serving utensils that had been brought out for the reception. When she finished, she made lists of still more things to do.

She viewed the piles of wedding gifts in the den with dismay. Every single one of them must be returned. After all there had been no wedding; there wouldn't be one. She saw so clearly how impossible marriage to Rodney would have been when she still had feelings for Ted.

The kitchen door banged loudly and her brother called out, "Anybody home?"

"In here."

Steve walked into the den and collapsed into a padded armchair. "You'll be happy to know *Kitten* didn't suffer too much damage in our little mishap. There's a small chunk of fiberglass knocked out of her bow—but it isn't serious. Hey—you doing okay?"

"I'm fine."

"You shouldn't feel so bad. What happened really wasn't your fault. I jammed the winch—remember?" There was a lengthy silence. "You called Rod to see how he's doing yet?"

"No, I haven't."

"You ought to, you know. You eaten?"

"No."

"Well, I'm going to grill a couple of cheese sandwiches. You want me to make one for you?"

"I don't think so, Steve. I'm really not very hungry."

"You ought to eat something. Might make you feel better."

"I'm fine—really."

"You sure as heck don't act like it," he said in exasperated tones.

He pulled himself out of the chair as if it were an effort and headed for the kitchen. She knew she wasn't good company, but she couldn't help it.

Steve was right. She should call Rodney. She'd already put it off too long. She dialed the number of the hospital and asked for the extension.

"He . . . Hello," Rodney answered in his tiniest voice.

Kit always marveled that Rodney, a big blond fellow who looked more like a baby-faced Norseman than a Texas rancher, could produce such a small sound.

"Hello, Rodney. This is Kit. How're you feeling?"

"I'm doing better," he said almost bravely. "The doctor's going to release me later this afternoon. I could come by your house on my way home. It would give us a chance to talk."

Seeing Rodney today was the last thing she needed.

"Rodney, I really don't know if we have that much to talk about today," she blurted.

"You're angry because I didn't show up at the wedding."

"'Angry' isn't the right word, Rodney," she said gently. "I'm having serious doubts about us, and I think you are too. I'm not at all sure but that your accident wasn't a 'blessing in disguise.'" She was using the same turn of phrase her father had. "We may have both been saved from making a terrible mistake."

There, she'd said it. A strained silence followed.

"I've been wondering about that myself, Kit," Rodney said at last. Did she hear relief in his voice? "Freud says there's no such thing as an accident. Lately I'd done quite a bit of thinking about us, but I didn't know how to talk to you about it. You seemed so enthusiastic about the wedding, so caught up in the preparations for it. You and your mother were working so hard, I just didn't have the heart . . ."

"Oh, Rodney, you should have."

"I'm a coward, Kit. You know that."

"No more than I . . ."

Although they talked a few minutes longer, there was nothing more to say. When she hung up her engagement was broken.

She turned her attention once more to the wedding gifts. She began separating the gifts from friends who lived nearby from the ones that would have to be wrapped for mailing.

Ted—if only she dared call him and find out about his arm. But he had been so cold, she lacked the courage.

She forced her mind away from Ted and back to the task of separating the gifts. She piled the gifts that would have to be mailed into a mountain. Oh! Surely there wasn't enough brown paper in all the world! This would take days!

She remembered her father's dinner invitation to Ted. Of course he wouldn't consider coming, but if he did. . . . The thought was disturbing.

The light in the sky had softened when she finally gave up her attempts to wrap the gifts. Six neatly addressed brown packages sat beside the mountain still to be wrapped.

"Nevertheless, six is a start," she thought wearily as she headed to her room.

Though she still wasn't hungry, she was exhausted. She changed clothes, folding her jeans, blouse, and scarf neatly and placing them on her bureau before slipping into a caftan that was flowing scarlet. She belted in her tiny waist with a golden sash. She smiled at her reflection, and the effect was dazzling. The brilliant color brought out her dark beauty. She brushed her hair until it was a wave of black satin falling to her shoulders. She looked exotic—like a Spanish princess.

She twirled in front of the mirror exactly as Ted always used to have her twirl when she'd dressed up for him. If only he could see her now! She smiled again, thinking of the way his eyes had always lit with admiration when he thought her especially attractive.

Then her smile faded, for he would never see her wear the caftan. His eyes would never light with pleasure. She remembered his coldness. Her heart began to beat jerkily as a feeling of hopelessness descended on her. The smartest thing she could do would be to put him out of her mind . . . permanently.

She sank—exhausted—into the softness of her bed. Her mind went blank. She was too tired to think of anything or of anyone, and she fell asleep almost at once.

She dreamed of a man who was tall and dark with strips of gold in his auburn hair. He was twirling her in his arms. She was a blaze of scarlet and gilt. He was laughing and so was she. Then their laughter faded, and they were breathless. His gaze became intense, yet tender. He was holding her tightly and she lifted her face to his kisses. He was so hard and so warm. Yet his lips felt infinitely soft as he nuzzled them against hers.

In her sleep, she smiled. She tossed and murmured his name. Only vaguely did she grow aware of a jarring clamor in the background.

Slowly, reluctantly she awoke. The blue princess telephone was jangling on her nightstand. She fumbled for the receiver and lifted it to her face.

"Hello," she murmured, her voice still thick with sleep.

"Is Howard Jackson there?" The deep, rich tones were unmistakably Ted's.

Clearly he had no wish to speak to her.

"I . . . I don't know," she said. "I'll have to check."

"No. Wait. Kit, is that you?"

"Yes."

"You didn't sound like yourself. I can give you the message just as easily. I'm calling to accept your father's invitation to dinner for Wednesday evening. I'll be bringing Phyllis."

"Oh," she said in a small voice.

"What time should we come?"

"We usually have dinner around seven."

"We'll be there."

He was about to hang up when she stopped him.

"Ted, did you see a doctor?"

"I just got in from the hospital. I have a spiral fracture of the humors in medical jargon. I'll be in a cast for a month or so."

"Oh, no! I . . . I'm very sorry about everything."

"Don't be. A broken arm is a small price to pay for having rescued a damsel in distress—surely."

"I don't know what to say."

"Don't say anything. Just be thankful that I have such a forgiving nature. A lot of men would have been glad to see a woman who'd been as troublesome to them as you have been to me sink beneath the waves and drown."

"I'm sorry I wrecked *Wild Lady*. I know how proud you were . . ."

"Were you always so obtuse or are you deliberately misunderstanding me?"

"What do you mean?"

"I'm not talking about *Wild Lady*. I'm talking about your jilting me five years ago without so much as a word of explanation or a good-bye."

"You know it wasn't like that."

"No, Kit, I don't."

She bristled at the hard note of accusal in his voice.

"Well, if I ran out on you it was exactly what you deserved! Thank goodness I realized what kind of man you were in time!"

"I think you realized you were falling for a poor man. In the nick of time you set your cap for Rodney, a bonafide Texas land baron who's filthy in oil and cattle."

This accusation infuriated her.

"I can't believe you have the nerve to accuse me of that when you know . . ."

"Know what, Kit? That you were used to the soft life. That you didn't want to risk marrying me and being poor?"

"Just because you have a complex about money, don't accuse me of it," she lashed out. "In the first place, you never mentioned marriage to me. In the second, I never had any intention of marrying Rodney for his money!"

"Then what are you marrying him for?" he hissed. "Love? Rodney does not seem like the type of man you would find . . . exciting."

She bit back the angry words that rushed to her lips.

His question went too deep. She'd almost told him that she'd only turned to Rodney out of loneliness in an attempt to forget *him*, the only man she'd ever loved. But that was something he must never never know. She would keep her pride intact at least, even if he'd broken her heart.

When she hesitated, he said, "You see . . . you want to continue living in your grand style, only grander. You know, Kit, when I first met you, I thought you were different. I thought you were the kind of girl . . . but now isn't the time to go into my foolish misconceptions about your character. I'll just say this morning was typical of our relationship—your ordering me to the servants' entrance . . . as if that's where I belong. I see very clearly that you're the type who gets a big thrill out of flaunting that large diamond you wear. With the Starr money behind you, you can have lots of diamonds. You can go anywhere, do anything, have anything. Do you know what that makes you, Kit? Don't you know what women who sell themselves are called?"

"Don't say it!" she cried. "Don't you dare say it! You don't understand me at all! If either of us had faulty character, it's you."

With that she slammed the phone down onto the receiver and lay back against her pillows as hot and angry as a curl of flame.

How different from her dream was the reality of her relationship with him!

Kit half expected Ted to call back and cancel on the dinner party, but he didn't. By Wednesday afternoon she was a nervous wreck. He would be coming in just a few hours. How could she face him now that she knew how he felt about her? She tried to comfort herself by rationalizing that she had an equally terrible opinion of him.

That evening she dressed carefully. She selected a low-cut, emerald-green sundress with a tightly fitting bodice that clung to her breasts and narrow waist. It had a full skirt that swirled in graceful folds below her knees. She slipped into green high-heeled sandals that accentuated the shapely curves of her legs as well as the daintiness of her ankles. She brushed her hair until it sparked like blue-black fire. Her skin glowed like rich cream, and her black eyes were sparkling as if she were actually looking forward to the dinner party instead of dreading it.

At the precise hour of seven when the library clock was chiming, the doorbell buzzed. Once and then again. She realized with dismay she would have to answer it because Steve and her father were out by the pool getting the charcoal fire started and her mother was in the kitchen with the cook. She dashed nervously toward the door, her green skirts flying, the rapid tappings of her high heels clicking on the saltillo tile.

She flung the door open wide. Lounging with menacing ease against a pillar like a great, dark tiger with a bandaged paw, was Ted. His tall, muscular build seemed to fill the doorway, his large presence dwarfing her. Navy slacks snugly fitted his narrow hips; the crisp cloth of his pale blue shirt stretched across the width of his firmly muscled chest.

His bold, sardonic gaze swept downward over her from the softly oblique line her black hair drew against the smoothness of her forehead, slowly over her body to the tips of her toes neatly buckled into their green sandals. His eyes lit with appreciation, and he whistled softly.

She gasped. She went warm all over and hated

herself and him as well because he could so easily fluster her.

"You look very nice tonight," he said silkily. "But you certainly took your time answering the door." When she still said nothing: "Aren't you going to ask us in?"

She felt curiously weak all over. Why did her senses respond in such a way to this infuriating man?

"Yes . . . of course. Where's Phyllis?"

"She had to go back to the car to get her purse. Oh, here she is."

"Hello, Phyllis," Kit said as graciously as she could under the circumstances. "Won't you come in?"

Phyllis gave an abrupt little shake of her head which Kit took to be a nod of agreement. The girl kept her smouldering gray eyes downcast as if she disliked Kit so intensely she had no wish to even look at her.

"Mother's in the kitchen. Steve and Daddy are outside lighting the fire," Kit said, attempting to cover the awkwardness with small talk. "Could I fix you a drink?"

"I'd like a beer," Ted said smoothly as if he felt perfectly at ease. "Phyllis, how about you?"

"Nothing, thank you," she managed.

Kit led the guests out onto the patio where Howard and Steve welcomed them. Then she escaped into the kitchen. Her mother was pouring ice tea into glasses.

"Mother, I can do that." Kit pulled a beer out of the refrigerator. "Why don't you take this out to Ted."

"*Querida,* don't you want to?"

Sharply: "No."

Her mother looked at her quizzically. "*Querida,* sometimes I don't understand you at all. When I was your age I would have wanted to take a drink out to a man like Ted Bradley."

Kit's hand that gripped the pitcher of iced tea shook. "Please! Mother!"

Kit tried to find things to busy herself with in the kitchen to avoid going out onto the patio. She'd never learned to cook and usually avoided it. She was placing rolls on cookie tins when she was startled by Ted's voice—vibrant and deep—directly behind her.

"If only you were wearing a ruffled apron you'd be the picture of domesticity, Kit. Somehow this new you is a surprise."

"Is it?" she replied without amusement. Why did he have to make the situation more difficult than it already was? She knew he disliked her. Why couldn't he just leave her alone?

"I think you're deliberately avoiding me," he said with alarming accuracy.

"And would that surprise you after our telephone conversation? I would think you would at least apologize for insulting me so . . ."

"I never apologize for the truth."

"That wasn't the truth."

"Wasn't it?" There was a watchful, puzzling glint in his blue eyes as if he found something about her difficult to understand.

"What did you come in here for anyway?"

"Phyllis changed her mind about that drink after all. She wants a beer."

"You'll find one in the refrigerator."

He opened the refrigerator door and pulled out a beer. Then—beer in hand—he came toward her. Although he was smiling, he looked ruthless . . . menacing. She was stiffening.

"You needn't bother to avoid me, Kit. If I want your company I'll seek it."

He was pivoting to leave her, when several ice cubes

slipped through her shaking fingers and splattered onto the floor. He stooped and retrieved them for her, tossing them carelessly into the sink on his way out.

His meaning was obvious. She wouldn't have to avoid him, because he had no intention of seeking her out. His words hurt—much more than they should have.

He was so coolly arrogant, so supremely self-confident—so indifferent to her now . . .

Throughout dinner the talk centered around racing although any mention of the accident was scrupulously avoided. Steve, Howard, and Ted were enjoying one another's company immensely. Anitra laughed merrily when one of the men made a joke. Only Phyllis—who stared moodily down at her untouched dinner plate when she wasn't glowering at Kit—and Kit failed to enjoy themselves.

After dinner the group moved into the den. Kit helped her mother serve after-dinner drinks. The men continued to discuss sailing. During a heated debate over the proper headsail to use in heavy air her father began to search through his stacks of sailing magazines for one issue in particular that had an article in it that would illustrate the point he was trying to make. Suddenly he remembered where it was. He was on the way to get it, when the telephone rang. It was a business call for him. He placed his hand over the receiver and summoned Kit.

"Kitten, would you mind going into the library and seeing if that September issue isn't on the table?"

"Not at all." She was only too glad to escape.

Her father excused himself to take the call in another room.

Ted was staring at her when she left the room, her hips swaying provocatively beneath the soft fabric of her green skirts. She walked self-consciously down the hall toward the library; self-conscious because she knew that he was still watching her in that boldly intent way of his and that he would continue to watch her until she vanished from his sight.

Why did he take such pleasure in annoying her?

She was rummaging through the magazines on one of the library tables, when Ted entered the room. She whirled to face him. He closed the double doors behind him so that they were completely alone together in the library.

His virile, blue gaze held hers until she looked quickly away. Every inch of him was handsome, she thought weakly. Why did he have to be so impossible? She steeled herself against his appeal as she remembered his accusations.

"Did you think you'd found another chance to escape?" he asked softly. He was smiling and she somehow found this apparent attempt at friendliness even more disturbing than when he'd been insulting.

"You heard my father," she replied coolly.

"Looks like he's going to be tied up on the phone for quite a while. That will give us a chance to talk."

"We have absolutely nothing to talk about."

"That's where you're wrong. I noticed you aren't wearing Rodney's ring tonight. Could it be that you found our conversation enlightening, and you've decided to mend your ways?"

"I found our conversation thoroughly disagreeable and not at all enlightening. I had already broken the engagement to Rodney *before* you called."

"Really? Why?"

"Because . . ." She broke off disconcerted. What could she say? She had no intention of telling him that her feelings for him had been the chief reason for her decision.

"I suppose you felt humiliated by the way he stood you up at the altar."

"That wasn't the reason."

"Then . . . what was the reason?"

"It's none of your business."

"Well, nevertheless, the important thing is that you're free again. I'd like to ask you out. Say tomorrow night. Why don't you come over to my place, and I'll cook dinner for you. If you weren't after Rodney's money, I'd like to know exactly why you ran out on me five years ago—not that it's important any longer. I'd just like to clear the slate."

"I can't believe you're asking me to dinner after the way you insulted me. I don't want to have anything more to do with you."

There was only the faintest tightening at the corners of his mouth. Then his lips curled as blue eyes that were too-knowing swept her. "You kissed me too passionately Sunday morning for me to believe that."

"Oh . . . Oh . . ." She was sputtering.

His voice drawled languidly. "I think you owe me one night. After all I broke my arm saving your neck, and you did wreck *Wild Lady*."

"Oh, all right. . . . When you put it like that."

"We'll make it at eight o'clock. That'll give me time to pack Missy off to Phyllis's so we can be alone."

"Where do you live?"

"You won't have any trouble finding it. I just moved into a townhouse south of here a bit . . . on Ocean Drive . . ." He told her the number.

Then he leaned forward, the contours of his muscles rippling beneath his crisp shirt as he picked up the

September issue of the sailing magazine. "I imagine your father is off the phone and will be wondering where the two of us are. He's going to have to work to prove his point. He's dead wrong about that headsail!"

"You don't think you make mistakes, do you?"

He looked up at her quickly and something—some emotion she couldn't read—came and went in the depths of his eyes. The moment was fleeting. His expression hardened almost at once, "Oh, I wouldn't say that." His tone was derisive, and a flicker of uneasiness raced down her spine. "I made one about you, didn't I?"

His words were shattering—like a bullet searing the soft tissue of her heart.

He left her then badly shaken from their conversation. Her date with him would serve as his brand of punishment for past grievances. How would she endure it—knowing that he disliked her?

She tried to cheer herself with the thought that it would only be one night—a few hours.

What could possibly happen in a few hours?

Chapter Five

Kit—the tires of her Porsche squealing—swerved onto the ribbon of asphalt winding down to the bay toward Ted's townhouse. She was late because she'd taken such pains with her appearance. This morning when she'd gone through her wardrobe she'd realized she didn't have anything special enough for tonight. Remembering how Ted had always admired her in bright colors she'd gone shopping and bought a new red dress. She'd justified the expense with the thought that if she was going to do battle with one of the most impossibly arrogant men she knew, she needed all her feminine armor intact.

And it was intact. Her freshly shampooed hair caught by a red silk headband fell in soft, raven clouds to her shoulders. Gauzy red cloth drifted over her curves, clinging, revealing, enhancing. She knew Ted would think the rich color brought out her dark beauty. The top of the dress was strapless and elasticized so that it molded her breasts and slender waist; the soft fabric of the skirt was swirling accordion pleats. She'd applied perfume, Ted's favorite scent.

But in spite of the dress she felt apprehensive. After all it was only armor. She still had to battle her dragon.

Uneasily she remembered last night and how he'd bested her. She remembered his parting words—words that had cut her deeply—when he'd said he'd made a mistake about her. She hadn't been able to forget either his words or the contemptuous tone of his voice when he'd spoken them. If only she didn't care what he thought of her!

Well, tonight . . . tonight wasn't going to be a repeat performance of last night, she vowed silently to herself. She was going to be careful to be polite but impersonal. How, exactly, she could accomplish this, was unclear.

Again tires squealed. She was driving too fast and all because she was late and nervous about her dinner date with Ted. She knew that in spite of all her careful plans to keep their conversation on safe topics and thereby preserve her composure, Ted would be in charge of the evening, and the evening would go as he directed it.

The drive curved unexpectedly, and a blur of red bounced directly in front of her. Kit—mindlessly terrified—stepped down on her brakes hard. The car slid to a standstill just as a pretty, dark-haired child bounded out from behind a parked car after the ball.

Kit put on the emergency brake and stepped from her car. The child was trying to retrieve her ball from a clump of Natal Plum.

"Ouch! Sticky!" The child turned toward Kit for help, the thorns and her ball her only concern. Her great cobalt-blue eyes implored—misting.

Kit was still not over her fright that she could have hit the child. She felt cold to the pit of her stomach. Her knees were so weak she almost wobbled as she walked toward the little girl. She pulled the ball from the brambles. The child's hands were eagerly outstretched.

Kit said, "Darling, you mustn't. . . . You mustn't ever. . . ." She was shaking so much, even her words seemed to shake. "You mustn't chase this ball just anywhere. If the ball goes into the street, please don't run after it. Not ever! Go get your mother . . ."

Before she could finish the child seized the ball and said defiantly in a voice quivering with pain; "My mother is dead." Then with the quickness of a little savage she darted away from Kit and disappeared toward the pool area.

Poor little thing! She was just a slip of a child. And no mother. She probably wasn't five years old. Such a spirited little darling with those saucy black curls framing that pixy face, those great big blue eyes.

Kit was still wondering vaguely who the child could belong to and why that person wasn't seeing after her properly as she climbed back into her car.

Slowly she drove toward Ted's townhouse. The color had gone out of the water and clouds; two flamingos, their great wings flapping languidly, were splashes of brilliant pink as they flew low over the darkening waves.

Kit pulled into a parking place not far from where she thought Ted's townhouse must be. She was still badly shaken from nearly having hit the child. She couldn't possibly face the ordeal of her date with Ted without giving herself a few minutes to calm down. She sat for a long time and watched the sun sink below the horizon. It was dark when she slung her purse over her shoulder and headed toward the townhouses. The breeze fanned her skirts, swirling them around her slender form.

The night was black velvet sprinkled with diamonds; the moonlight was silver ribbons spreading across the bay. And Kit, racing toward Ted's townhouse with the graceful lightness of a sea sprite, was as young and lovely as the night.

She paused, breathless. She was staring at the cluster of townhouses trying to determine which was Ted's. They were all so alike, great sloping shadows in the darkness, differing only in that some were unlighted and others lighted. Ted had called her earlier that afternoon and given her specific instructions how to locate his. She began to count the buildings and headed in the direction of one which was cheerily lit. Its large plate glass windows facing the bay were as brilliant as bars of glowing gold. She noticed the fuzzy shadow against the drapes of what looked like an etagère. Yes, it was his! She could make out the numbers above his lighted front door.

She knocked on his door several times and no one answered. She looked at her watch. She was a few minutes late. She'd been so upset over nearly running into the little girl that she'd sat in her car far too long.

She decided he might have stepped out for something. Perhaps he'd lacked some ingredient for the meal and when she'd been late, he'd decided to do a bit of last-minute grocery shopping. It never occurred to her he would stand her up. He'd been determined last night to make her accept his invitation, and then this afternoon when he'd called, he'd been equally forceful.

Perhaps something had happened. Well. . . . She waited another couple of minutes and then scribbled him a note and pinned it to his door. She decided to return to her car and drive down to a little convenience store where she'd spotted a pay phone and call him. Perhaps he'd been running late and was showering.

She headed back toward her car. She was almost to the pool when she saw out of the corner of her eye, a blur of something bounce toward the pool. In the distance—as if it came from the pool, she thought she heard a faint splash.

She turned from the pool in the direction of the parking lot. Suddenly she heard—again from the pool area—a squeal, desperate and high-pitched followed by a splash, larger than the one before.

And then—nothing. No sound other than the murmur of banana leaves rustling gently as the wind swept up from the bay.

She was about to hurry on toward her car, but something, some warning of danger, stopped her. She turned and saw floating quietly on the aqua waters of the pool like a cherry decorating a fancy drink, a bright red ball. She was remembering bright blue eyes thickly fringed with sable lashes set in the face of a pixy. Where was the little girl?

A quiver sliced through her. Truly afraid, Kit was running toward the pool. Beneath the ball, almost at the bottom of the lighted pool she saw something dark. Forgetting her watch and her purse, she plunged into the water with them and dragged the object to the surface.

She swam toward the shallow end of the pool, pulling the child with her. She lifted the little girl into her arms and carried her up the steps out of the pool. The child opened her mouth and gasped. She took a second breath. No water sputtered up. She was perfectly all right.

Hugging the little girl to her closely, Kit sank into one of the poolside chairs.

"I was holding my breath," the child explained brightly. "You didn't have to jump in 'cause I know how to swim. My daddy taught me."

The wind gusted around them and the two of them shivered with cold.

Kit remembered her purse—still at the bottom of the pool. She saw that her wrist was bare. Her watch must have fallen off in the scramble.

"I got you all wet," the child said. "And big people don't like to get wet. Your red dress is all ruined. Are you mad?"

"No, I'm just thankful you're all right."

She was remembering how carefully she'd dressed, how carefully she'd arranged her hair. She wouldn't be female if she didn't feel a twinge of dismay. She remembered her watch and purse. Still, those things were unimportant. . . . "You and that ball!" She hugged the child fiercely.

Then they were laughing—Kit a little hysterically and the child with sheer delight.

"I must get you home," Kit said at last. She would take the child home and go home and call Ted and explain why she couldn't make it tonight. She couldn't possibly face him now—looking as she did.

Reluctantly the child agreed. "We'll go to Daddy's house first." She skipped off toward a nearby town-house.

Kit was too distracted by everything that had happened to read the lighted numbers above the door.

She was ringing the doorbell when the child said, "Ever since my mother died I've lived with my Aunt Phyllis. Daddy lives next door. . . ."

Then the door opened and Kit was staring up into the boldest of blue eyes. Ted's handsome face went dark with alarm.

"Princess! Kit. . . . What happened?"

For one long moment Kit was too stunned for speech. Her red silk headband fell at a crazy angle across one eye. Her dress was dripping like a soaked dishcloth. Doubtless her eye make-up was smudged beneath her eyes. She remembered ruefully how she'd planned to be the picture of sophisticated composure this evening.

"My ball went into the pool," Missy cried. "Then I fell in trying to get it out, and the pretty lady jumped after me." The child hushed, breathless, and shivering in the air-conditioning.

"Your Aunt Phyllis has been looking everywhere for you, Missy." Ted said sternly. "You shouldn't have run off."

"I know," the child said, her big blue eyes—so like his—solemn.

"Kit, come inside. I'll call Phyllis and tell her Missy's safe. I'll find something dry for you to put on."

"That really isn't necessary. I'll just run on home."

"Oh, no you don't!" His good hand was on her elbow, and he propelled her into the room which was as boldly modern in decor as the architecture outside. "I got your note. The reason I wasn't here was because I was down on the beach searching for Missy. I don't know why I didn't leave the door unlocked."

She was vaguely aware of white walls on which hung large, abstract paintings, of sleek furniture done in earth tones, of brown carpet—plush—stretching across the room, of sheets of glass looking out onto the moonlit bay. And on the wall directly opposite the windows and over the sofa was an enormous slash of silver with beveled edges. The mirror was bold—like the house, like the man who lived in it. The mirror reflected the loveliness of the scene outside.

73

"I wouldn't dream of letting you go home like this, shivering. You'd catch pneumonia," Ted was saying.

He led her to a chair and overruled her protests that she was too wet to sit on it by saying that it was upholstered in leather and couldn't be hurt by a little water. He brought a blanket and wrapped her in it; he brought her a long-stemmed crystal goblet filled with amber liquid. He insisted that she drink it. Only too late—as it flowed scalding down her throat—did she realize it was brandy.

He was kneeling before her, his knees sinking deeply into the rich brown carpet. She saw that he was refilling her goblet.

His eyes were on her face and they were electric blue. She went warm all over. She was remembering again that other time—was it only Sunday?—when she'd been shivering with cold and they'd sat together beneath the blanket. She was dizzy suddenly. She was afraid to take the goblet from his hands because she was trembling. It was just the cold and the brandy combining . . . surely . . .

He was reaching beneath the blanket. He caught her wrist in his large brown hand. She knew he must feel the leap of her pulse as her heart quickened. Again she felt a treacherous warm tide of feeling wash over her.

He placed the goblet a second time in her hand, saying, "Just sit here and relax while I call Phyllis."

She sank back feeling cozy and cared for as he went to the phone. Slowly she sipped her brandy, watching him.

Tonight he wore black slacks and a shirt of the deepest blue—the color of his eyes. She saw the column of his dark throat above the unbuttoned top of his shirt. Once—when she'd felt like this—she would have been

free to press her lips against the warm flesh of his throat, and he would have drawn her into his arms and responded passionately.

Feeling strangely heavy, she placed the goblet on the glass table beside her and lay back against the chair.

He went to the telephone; and when he dialed Phyllis, there was no answer.

Missy, her black hair shining wet, was a bundle of exuberant energy bouncing into her lap and snuggling into her arms to share the warmth of her blanket.

"I've brought Joseph," the child said. She thrust a large, white, stuffed rabbit—a little worn from love—up for Kit to admire. "I want him to meet you."

"Hello, Joseph, I'm Kit."

"That's almost like cat. Rabbits like cats. Or anyway Joseph does, and he's a rabbit."

The child continued to chatter gaily, describing the peculiarities of Joseph's personality. Joseph wasn't an ordinary rabbit. He was special. And he didn't like carrots either. He preferred chocolate as apparently his little mistress did.

Kit, in turn, told the child a story. The child listened—rapt. Once while she was telling her the tale, Kit looked up and saw Ted watching them intently, but when he saw her look up, he turned quickly away.

Time passed pleasantly until Ted, who had finally reached Phyllis, decided it was time he took Missy to her aunt's.

Missy wanted to remain on Kit's lap and listen to another story. It was only with the greatest effort that Ted persuaded her to leave Kit to go to her Aunt Phyllis's. Missy was at the door holding her father's hand when she suddenly broke out of his embrace and raced back to Kit. Impulsively she flung her arms

around Kit's neck and kissed her on the nose. Then she was skipping nimbly back to her father.

Ted was gone for at least a quarter of an hour. His heavy footsteps sounding on the concrete walkway outside signaled his return. The door opened abruptly, and he entered the room. Kit heard the lock click firmly as he shot the bolt. Then he moved toward her with the silent, menacing grace of a large cat stalking his prey. She shrank against leather upholstery. She was alone with him, and she felt strangely alarmed. Her heart hammered wildly as if she were his prey.

Ted sank into the thick carpet at her feet.

"Sorry I was gone so long," he said in husky tones.

"That . . . th-that's all right . . ." she managed a little breathlessly because of his dangerous nearness. As always she felt powerless against his virile appeal. Just the proximity of his body to hers affected her senses.

His dark face was grave. "How can I ever repay you, Kit, for saving Missy?"

"It was nothing."

"It was everything . . . to me," he contradicted. His voice held an intimate quality that was even more unsettling to her than his nearness.

"Missy was in no danger. She said she was holding her breath."

"Missy is a poor swimmer at best. She can hold her breath like a champ, but if you hadn't come along when you did, I very much doubt if she could've gotten out of that pool alive."

"Oh, no!" She let out a little horrified gasp.

"So you see . . . how much I owe you." The tones of his voice were rich and deep—and unnervingly intimate. He was reaching beneath the blanket for her

hands. He took them in his, and as always at his touch she shivered. "You're cold. We've got to get you out of those clothes."

He drew her up from the chair and the blanket fell from her. He pulled her—unresisting—into the warmth of his arms and led her toward his bedroom.

Everything seemed to happen as if in a dream. She saw his bed—its headboard, gleaming chrome, its spread a vivid splash of blue, the very color of his eyes. It stood in the center of the vast room beneath a large painting of a pale blue sailboat flying before the wind. *Wild Lady* . . . before . . . the accident. Her eyes riveted to the bed.

Again she sensed the danger, and she stiffened in his arms. He led her toward his dressing room and bath area.

"I want you to relax. Take a warm bath. I'll go next door and get some dry clothes from Phyllis."

"Really . . . you mustn't . . . None of this is necessary. I'll just go on home. I'll be fine. Really I will." She finished through chattering teeth.

"You're in no condition to know what is necessary," he said firmly. "You're shaking like a leaf. I want you to do just as I say. You can leave your wet clothes . . ."

"Leave my wet clothes? As if it's perfectly all right for me to undress in your bedroom while we're here alone! What if someone were to come by and find me like that? One of your neighbors . . ."

"None of my neighbors would dream of coming over at this hour unless I invited them," he said smoothly. "And I have no intention of letting you catch your death of pneumonia because of your Victorian morals. It's clear to me that you think I might be planning to take advantage of this situation. But let me assure you,

I'm not. I'm deeply grateful to you, Kit, for what you did tonight. And I want to repay you by doing what anyone would do. I'm simply offering you the comfort and convenience of my home so you can bathe and change into something warm and dry. Is that so awful?"

He sounded almost hurt. His dark face was gravely handsome, his voice sincere. He was merely being courteous. She felt a pang of guilt to have doubted him.

"No, it isn't awful at all," she said weakly, feeling foolish for her unwarranted suspicions. "And it would be nice . . . very nice . . . to bathe and slip into dry things."

"I'm glad that's settled."

"Wait! My gold watch! And my purse!"

"What about them?"

"They're at the bottom of the pool . . ."

"I'll get them with the boat hook while you're bathing." He was at the door, pressing the button of the doorknob.

"There," he said. "When I pull the door closed, it will lock, and you'll be safe . . . from me." His lips parted in a broad, rakish grin that made her feel guiltily uncomfortable. It had always been easy for him to read her. She thought he was secretly amused because of her suspicions about him. Without saying another word, he left her, pulling the door shut behind him.

She went to the door and pressed her fingertips to the doorknob. He'd been as good as his word. It was locked. Feeling reassured and a trifle ashamed that she'd doubted him, she went to the dressing room area and began to undress.

She really was being frightfully cold to him. And he was being so good to her, so considerate. Ever since she'd arrived, he'd done nothing other than be solicitous of her every comfort. She remembered the blanket, the brandy. He was going to bring dry clothes. And more than anything, his gratitude to her for saving his child, had touched her. She removed her clothes and lay them on the marble counter in the dressing room.

Bare feet touched the cold baby-blue tile of his bathroom floor. Beige Turkish bathsheets hung on chrome bars. She turned on the water and fingered its warm flow until it was just the right temperature. She saw a child's jar of perfumed bubble bath on one corner of the tub. Missy's no doubt. Impulsively she sprinkled the bubble bath into the water, and then as the sweet-smelling bubbles began to build like a foam mountain, she slipped into the tub and lay back languidly.

For a long time—it seemed half an hour—she lay there soaking. She hadn't meant to, but the water was so warmly pleasant. And she had been blue with cold.

At last she forced herself to bathe and shampoo her hair. Then she stepped from the tub and wrapped herself in a thick Turkish bathsheet. She wound a smaller towel around her hair so that it looked like a turban. She unlocked the bathroom door, and as she stepped through the doorway, shining in the dressing room mirror was the vision of her own loveliness. She scarcely glimpsed the reflection of her breathtakingly beautiful face, the rosy flush of her cheeks, the crescent of gleaming black hair just visible beneath the folds of her turban.

Where were her clothes? Ted's clothing littered the bright blue bedspread.

She saw black slacks. She saw his blue shirt in a careless heap. His shoes . . . all thrown down as if he'd hastily undressed. Her own clothes were nowhere to be seen.

Then she heard the sound of music playing softly and drifting in from the living room. Her heart beat with short little spasms. It was the very music he'd played the night he'd almost made love to her so long ago. A saxophone was playing low and sexy.

She should have known she couldn't trust him! But he'd been so courteous, solicitous, so grateful to her for saving his child that she'd been taken in.

The music enveloped her and for one long moment she remembered the beauty of their last night together. Nothing he could have done other than play that music could have brought their time of love back more poignantly. Tears were in her eyes, and she lifted her fingers to push them away.

Oh, he was horrible! Horrible! Too horrible for words! Just the sound of that music brought back the hurt. How could he have played it?

She was filled with murderous fury. She was shaking with it. If he thought for one minute that he could seduce her just because he'd given her two glasses of brandy, tricked her into removing her clothes, and put on that record, he had another thought coming! She wasn't that weakly sentimental! And to think he'd used his child, to accomplish this! He was low and it was obvious he had a poor opinion of her as well.

Holding the bathsheet tightly so that it couldn't fall, she rushed to the door. She saw that strangely the small button in the doorknob was still pressed down. How had he gotten in? Never mind. . . . His type knew all the tricks. There was no time like the present to give him a piece of her mind. She'd set him straight once and for all about the kind of girl she was.

She heard sounds from the living room, but she ignored them. She opened the door and called loudly, "Ted, you bring me my clothes this minute. I'd like to get dressed and go home before someone comes and finds me . . ."

"I'll just bet you would!"

"Phyllis!" she was gasping. "What . . . what are you doing here?"

"I could ask you the same question if the answer wasn't all too apparent!" Phyllis was pale with rage; every inch of her quivered with that same emotion. "In answer to *your* question: The door was wide open so I came in to get Missy's ball. When she remembered she'd left it here, she refused to go to sleep until I promised to come over and get it."

Kit scanned what she could see of the living room for any sign of Ted, but she couldn't find him. Where in Heaven's name was he? Surely if he could be found, he would explain.

"Phyllis, this isn't what you think. It's all perfectly innocent."

"Innocent?" She was pushing past Kit and striding into the bedroom. Her eyes were on Ted's clothes. Then she returned to the living room. "You must have a strange definition for that word. It's plain as day what's going on." She turned to face Kit once more. "I should have known you'd try something like this! Your ego just can't take the fact that a man jilted you—"

Kit drew a sharp, quick breath and flinched. She couldn't blame Phyllis for drawing the conclusion she had. She herself was convinced that Ted had not planned an *innocent* evening. But she couldn't understand why Phyllis was so hostile . . . unless . . . she were interested in Ted for herself. Aloud she said, "For your information, trapping Ted is the last thing I have on my mind at the moment. Where is he anyway? He'll set you straight."

"You tell me. It's obvious you *know* him . . . far better than I do."

"Oh . . ." Kit was angry too, and she was finding it increasingly difficult to hold her temper in check.

Just then the door leading into the kitchen from the utility room and garage opened and closed. Both women heard the refrigerator door open. Then Ted, holding a news magazine in his good hand and an unopened beer in the other, stepped into the living room. At first he did not notice the girls because he was avidly reading an article in the magazine. Then setting the magazine on the counter, but continuing to read, he opened his beer. Kit sighed loudly and impatiently as he flipped a page. He looked up.

His lazy gaze took in Phyllis—still white and quivering with rage—as well as Kit clad only in his towel, and he smiled. His smile, which Kit was sure was motivated by amusement rather than friendliness, only infuriated her the more.

She saw that he was dressed only in a thick velour blue robe, its wide sleeves concealing his cast. His chest—tanned and muscled—was a V of darkness against the blue of his robe where it opened down the front.

Her mouth went slack. She couldn't believe what she was seeing. What was he doing in that robe? His hair was wet and rumpled—as if he too had bathed or showered . . . perhaps with her . . . or as if she'd run her hands through it while they'd made love. In spite of her anger she was aware of an odd breathlessness at the sight of him—so virile and overpoweringly masculine dressed only in his robe.

With a look of dry amusement curving his lips, he lifted the magazine from the table and would have resumed reading it had not Kit snatched it from his hand and tossed it onto the carpet.

"Ted . . . what are you . . . but never mind. . . . Tell Phyllis . . . tell her the truth about us . . . and what happened here tonight."

"Don't be ridiculous! Phyllis doesn't expect an explanation." He moved across the room to the stereo and turned it down.

"Tell her the truth," Kit hissed.

"All right," he said lazily.

Phyllis interrupted him with a burst of impatience. "Ted, you're absolutely right. I have no interest in hearing an explanation. What you do is your own affair."

Ted lifted his beer can to his lips. Then he settled himself into his large overstuffed chair as if that finished the matter.

"Put that down and tell her!" Kit cried.

"All right . . . if you insist. Do you mind if I make myself comfortable first?" He plumped a cushion under his cast with maddening slowness. "The blasted thing is awfully heavy." He turned toward Phyllis. "The facts are quite straightforward. Kit was the one who jumped into the pool to save Missy. Her clothes got wet in the process, and she decided to take a bath and change . . ."

Phyllis couldn't resist a question. "Isn't that Kit's red dress on your sofa?"

Kit saw the rumple of bright red—her dress! Her undergarments—dry now—were also piled on the sofa.

"Those clothes certainly look dry to me," Phyllis commented.

"They are *now*," Ted said quietly.

Phyllis caught the edge in his voice and relented. "Well, as I said earlier—what the two of you do or don't do . . . is none of my business. What I *would* like to know is where's Missy's ball. I promised I'd find it for her."

"It's in the kitchen sink," Ted said. He waved one hand toward the cubicle brightly covered in foil wallpaper that was his kitchen.

Phyllis went to the kitchen and returned with the ball. Ted got up and joined her at the door. "Phyllis, bear with me . . ." Ted said. "I can see by Kit's scowl that she isn't at all happy with the way I've explained things. I can't let you leave without putting this mess in the proper perspective. As a woman you should understand how much importance women attach to morals and their reputations. No matter how things look . . . I have the most honorable of intentions toward Kit."

"Really, Ted, I told you none of this is necessary . . ." Phyllis said faintly.

"Nevertheless . . ." Ted insisted, opening the door for her. "I will tell you. I had wanted Kit's parents to be the first to know . . . but under the circumstances and because you are family . . . I'm going to marry Kit."

Chapter Six

"I'm going to marry Kit." Ted's words rang in Kit's mind. Had he gone mad?

Phyllis had practically collapsed against him when he'd said that. The poor girl had looked shattered as he'd led her from his townhouse to her own.

"I thought she'd never leave," Ted said, interrupting Kit's thoughts. He was shooting the bolt in the front door after Phyllis had gone. "We're alone at last!"

His eyes went over her, forcing an awareness in her of her body and his virile response to it. Worse still, he forced her to be aware of her own answering response to him. His voice went deep and husky. "Do you have any idea what the sight of you in that . . . only that . . . does to me, Kit?"

She felt curiously light-headed, treacherously aroused by his words.

His large brown hand was on the dimmer of the light switch. As if by magic the lights dimmed to a romantic glow. He came toward her. The dim light caused a shadow to flicker across his dark features.

She watched him—mesmerized. Her pulses quickened in anticipation. She was unable to prevent the flush which swept her cheeks, but she managed to meet his gaze which was as direct as ever.

"Don't come near me!" she cried breathlessly. His eyes were on her fingers nervously clutching the towel about her. "*You* stay away from me!" She was terribly aware of the feel of terry against her breasts, of the feel of it—soft—against the smooth flesh of her body. Oh, if only she were properly dressed, she wouldn't feel at such a disadvantage.

"You're shrinking against that chair with all the terror of a prim virgin who thinks she is about to be . . ." The omitted word hung in the vast silence of the room. She saw his teeth flash white in the darkness. "Odd; but I have the distinct impression you're scared of me, Kit."

"Ted Bradley!" She stiffened with outrage. She longed to be able to honestly refute that remark. He was so smug; he felt himself so superior to her. "I'm not afraid of you! I'm . . . I'm angry. . . . Furious. . . ."

"Then I want to know why you're so angry at me?" he asked innocently.

She watched with wild relief as he sank down into his overstuffed chair instead of coming nearer to her. Thank heavens he'd decided *for once* to follow her bidding! She felt on much safer ground.

"As if you don't know."

"I don't. That's why I'm asking."

"You tricked me out of my clothes pretending to be grateful about Missy."

"I was grateful. And I didn't trick you out of your clothes."

"Then while I was taking a bath you removed my clothes . . ."

"Only to put them in the dryer," he replied with an easiness that only angered her the more.

"And you took off your own and threw them on the bed."

"I couldn't reach your purse and watch from the edge of the pool with the boat hook. I had to change into my swimming trunks—which strangely enough I keep in my bedroom." He opened his robe so that she could see he was wearing his bathing suit under it.

"Well, you put on that record . . . that same record you played the last night . . ." She was becoming flustered.

"It happens to be a favorite of mine."

"And where are the clothes you promised to get from Phyllis?" she countered, determined to catch him.

"I didn't think it would be necessary to involve Phyllis since you took such a long bath and yours were dry before you finished."

"You didn't bring them to me . . ."

"Would you have wanted me to? You were bathing, remember. I thought you might object if I showed up in the bedroom when you were getting out of the tub. And I can see by the way you're overreacting to all this, that you would have."

Kit thought she detected a barely perceptible smile on his face, mocking her. She blushed furiously. He always bested her!

"You have an answer for everything," she said, admitting her defeat.

"Are you quite finished with your interrogation?" he asked after a brief silence. He was no longer smiling;

his blue gaze raked her thoroughly and she remembered with a start all she wore was his towel. When she said nothing: "What I want to know is why you would think I would do all the things you've accused me of? What have I ever done . . ."

"As if you don't know . . ."

"I don't. And I'm getting sick of all your insinuations—that I mistreated you in the past. When it was you who walked out on me."

"I don't want to talk about the past."

"Why not? Have you developed a conscience after all these years?"

His steady gaze probed her face for the answers she refused to give him. His calm, deliberate manner was unnerving.

"I want to go home."

She was edging slowly toward the puddle of bright red cloth on the sofa, but, before she could reach it, he read her mind. He sprang from his chair and seized her clothes. The flimsy material of her undergarments flowed through his fingers and fell upon the carpet. His blue eyes, lazy with amusement, gazed down at them and then up at her. She was increasingly aware—and by his expression it was evident he was too—that she was naked but for his towel. She felt her cheeks grow warm. Oh, if only he wouldn't look at her like that!

"Give me my clothes so I can go."

"You're very beautiful when that Latin temper of yours catches fire."

"Give them to me!"

He sat back down in his chair, still holding her dress. A brief grin curving the corners of his mouth teased her.

"Sit down and relax. You're not going anywhere yet!"

"You would keep me here against my will?"

"Until you hear me out."

"I've heard all I want to hear for one night."

"Not quite. Unless you intend to run out of here naked without your car keys. I'm certainly in no mood to loan you that towel."

"You took my keys?"

"I didn't take them. I retrieved them from the pool along with your purse and watch." She heard a faint jingle as he held them up for her to see. He smiled pleasantly. "I suppose you could go knock on one of my neighbors' doors. I'm sure you'd find someone willing to help you."

"You're . . . insolent and crude." He only laughed. "You think all of this is hilarious. Phyllis will probably tell everyone she knows. What if she calls my family— as if there hasn't been enough gossip about me. I'll never be able to hold my head up in this town."

"Phyllis would never do anything like that, and I think you're attaching too much importance to what unimportant people think."

"You couldn't possibly understand. You don't have a decent bone in your body. You're twisted . . . and horrible . . . and . . . and . . ." She failed to think of an adequate insult.

"I get the picture. But if you're quite through with your insults, I have a plan to help you, a plan that will be the salvation of your reputation."

"I think you've done more than enough for one evening."

"Nevertheless, hear me out. *You can marry me.*"

"What?"

"You heard me. *You can marry me.*"

For that she had no answer. She lapsed into a moment of stunned silence.

He'd said something to Phyllis about marrying her. But she'd thought it a crazy taunt; she hadn't believed he'd been serious. She saw now that he had meant it. His dark face was grave as if he'd never been more serious in all of his life. He was watching her face intently as if he were hanging on her next words, as if he were hoping she would say . . . What? What could such a perverse human hope for under the circumstances? His proposal was outrageous!

Never had she felt further from understanding him than she did at this moment. He looked expectant, almost eager as if her answer were very important to him, as if this were a bonafide proposal . . .

And how . . . how could she answer him under the circumstances? She felt a strange eagerness as she wouldn't have dreamed she could at his words. They seemed to ring in her ears like music. *"You can marry me. You can marry me."* And for some idiotic reason marriage to him seemed like the most natural thing in all the world.

Nothing that had happened in the past few days seemed to matter beside that. She no longer cared that Rodney had jilted her. All that was important was that Ted, Ted had asked her to marry him.

She fought against the emotions that were sweeping her, the old familiar weakening, the hunger for his touch. She loved him as she had never loved Rodney. Why hadn't she realized it before? Rodney was just a man she'd spent time with because she couldn't have the man she really loved. Without Ted her life had been empty. Even though he'd been infuriating these past few days, she'd felt alive as she hadn't since he'd left her. She'd felt! And for five years she'd felt nothing.

Now she knew by her powerful emotional response

to his proposal that her feelings for Ted stemmed from love.

But there was so much she didn't understand. Letitia. His marriage. His abrupt reappearance in her life. What were his motives behind this proposal? She would be foolish to assume he was romantically attracted to her just because she was in love with him. He couldn't love her. Nor had he mentioned love to her.

He must have some other reason—other than love—for wanting to marry her.

She was remembering the past: that golden, scarlet, crisp October when she'd fallen in love with him. He'd courted her ardently, pretending to love her so cleverly. She'd never detected he had the slightest interest in any other woman. She'd been so young and naive—easy prey for a man like him.

Then she'd found out about Letitia, and she'd run from him. Later she'd learned from friends that Ted's adopted father had died. Ted dropped out of law school then because he didn't have enough money to continue his education and help his mother. Mrs. Bradley had given her son all the insurance money from her husband's death, and Ted had started his own business. He'd married and begun a life that no longer included Kit.

Just thinking of it and she was hurting again as if it were only yesterday. Clearly she'd just been one of many women in Ted's life. No! He wasn't asking her to marry him for love. She knew him too well to believe that. He had some other less noble motive. What was it?

"At least you didn't say 'no' right off the bat," Ted said, breaking into her thoughts. "That's something."

"Well, I should have." It would never do to let him

suspect how vulnerable she felt where he was concerned. She actually—fool that she was—wanted to marry him. She loved him. *She loved him.* The realization was still new to her. What would he do if he knew the extent of his power over her? The thought hardened her voice. "I wouldn't marry you if you were the last man on earth. If I didn't know before how terrible you are I do now."

"And what have I done that's so terrible? Would you prefer me to kneel before you and take your hand in mine and beg you to marry me? Yes, that's it. I can see it shining in your eyes. You're an incurable romantic, Kit."

Before she could do anything other than gasp in horror he sprang from his chair and was kneeling at her feet. She shrank back into her chair as he seized her hand, her free hand that wasn't fearfully clutching terry cloth around her.

"Why, Kit you're trembling."

"If I'm trembling, it's with rage." She pulled frantically at her hand, but he held it tightly.

"I don't think so. You're trembling because I'm touching you. Remember, I know you." He hesitated. "You were thinking earlier that I was planning to seduce you, weren't you?"

Her eyes widened at this truth.

"And I'm wondering if that isn't what you secretly longed for. I haven't forgotten our kiss in the drive," he continued softly.

"No. . . . No . . ." She was backing away from him. She tried to draw the edges of the towel closer about her body. If only he wasn't so near. If only she could escape from him. But where? Where could she go without her clothes? To his bedroom? She could lock him out. She knew from experience that wouldn't work.

He increased the pressure of his grip. He was pulling her from the chair, down onto the carpet beside him.

"There . . . that's better. I'm tired of playing games, Kit. I want you as I've never wanted any woman. And you want me too."

"I don't want you! I don't!" Her pulse raced, mocking her swift denial.

"We're going to settle this argument tonight once and for all."

"Oh, no!"

He was pushing her body down onto the thick pile of the carpet and positioning her beneath himself. Oh! He knew exactly what he was doing! She struggled wildly, but he was far stronger. And he held her beneath him almost effortlessly. She was panting with fury and with something that went deeper than fury, something he was deliberately trying to awaken.

His good fingers closed around her fingers that were holding the edges of the towel together and he ripped the towel from her body so that she lay naked beneath him. Carelessly, triumphantly he flung it aside. His gaze swept insolently from her blazing eyes, over her breasts, across the flat of her stomach, down the curve of her thighs. He missed nothing. "You're beautiful, Kit. Even more beautiful than I remembered." As she cried out he muffled her cry with his lips. She pushed against his chest but it was like iron. She tried to toss her head, so that he could not kiss her, but he brought his good hand up and held her face still. His kiss was long and searching and she writhed—but in vain—to escape him. His lips left hers, and he was murmuring endearments in his softest, huskiest voice.

"Kit, I've been such a fool. . . . We've wasted so many years."

She was about to answer him, but his mouth closed over hers once more. He was parting her lips with his tongue. His kisses became urgent and possessive, ruthless. Her hands were reaching up and circling his neck. She was pulling him to her tightly. She felt the hard warmth of his lean body, and thick hairs of his chest—bristly—against the rounded softness of her breasts.

She was shivering as if she were cold, but she was warm. He had been out of her life for five years, but her body remembered the delight of his and betrayed her. She was opening her mouth and kissing him as passionately as he was kissing her. All of her resistance against him was flowing out of her. She wanted him; she couldn't help herself. She loved him as much as the night she'd loved him so long ago when she—thinking their love would last forever—had almost given herself to him.

She forgot his treachery and was only aware of the feel of his hand moving gently over her, tracing the supple curves of her body. She felt his lips on hers. Then he was kissing her on her cheek, her neck, her earlobe. She felt his breath—warm—in her hair.

Oh, she wanted him; and he knew it. Her heart was beating fiercely, joyously as she waited for him to possess her.

Then, just as she thought he would take her, he seemed to catch himself and stop. He shuddered violently. Then he held her to him, breathing deeply as if to check his passion, before he pushed her roughly away. Blindly she saw him grab the bathsheet from the sofa and pull it over her.

"I think I've proved my point," he said brutally.

"What?" She felt stunned; cheated. She'd been on the verge of surrendering herself to him because she loved him, and he'd been trying to prove a point.

"I wanted to prove to you once and for all that you want me as much as I want you. And I think—stubborn though you can be—even you will admit I'm right now."

How could he . . . how could he . . .

"I won't admit . . ." she broke off, strangling. In another minute she would be crying. She had never felt so hurt, or so lost in her whole life.

"Admit it, or you might drive me to further lengths to prove it to you."

"I admit it," she said slowly, reluctantly. He smiled; his eyes were brilliant. "You needn't look so smug," she said in what she hoped was her coldest voice, "I only kissed you like that because I couldn't help myself. I . . ."

"Exactly. And I can't help myself where you're concerned either."

"That's no reason to ask me to marry you."

"I didn't say that was why I was asking you to marry me. A man my age looks for more in marriage than that."

"I . . . I . . ." His face was blurring in tears. She tried unsuccessfully to blink them back. He hadn't meant any of his kisses. Even his passion for her was phony. He'd only used her to prove some idiotic point. He'd been playing a cruel game to boost his much-too-conceited ego. To prove his power over her. Now he was conversing as if nothing that had happened between them mattered to him. She began to weep bitterly and hated herself for doing so.

"Kit, darling. You're crying. I've hurt you."

He'd called her "darling."

Between sobs: "And no doubt that proves even further how susceptible I am where you're concerned."

He pulled her—unresisting because she was too upset to fight him—into his arms. His hand stroked her hair.

"No matter what you think, Kit, I don't want to hurt you. You're very special to me. That's why I'm not going to make love to you tonight even though I want you more than I've ever wanted anything." His whole body shook violently. I want you. You don't know what just holding you like this is doing to me. But this time I want things to be right between us. We're going to marry first."

She pushed against him and he let her go. She wanted to believe him, but because she wanted to so much, she couldn't let herself. Once long ago he'd betrayed her trust, and she couldn't allow herself to trust him again. She reminded herself he'd been kissing her as if he wanted her desperately, and he'd only been trying to prove a point. Wasn't trickery dishonesty? Didn't that prove he couldn't be trusted?

"Why do you want to marry me?" she blurted.

"Don't you know me well enough to know the answer to that?"

"No! I don't think I know you at all. I don't suppose I ever did, even though once, I thought I did. You pretended to love me, when all the time . . ."

As always when the past was mentioned, his face darkened. His lips twisted into a grim, cynical smile. "I think you and I would do best to forget the past," he said evenly. "Our discussions about it always dead-end. Let's sum it up by saying we both made mistakes, but if we've learned from them, we don't have to repeat them. As for why I want to marry you, I have my own reasons. But I'd rather not discuss them now. We'll discuss them over dinner."

He'd talked about mistakes. Did he mean he was a changed man? Did he mean he wouldn't turn to another woman if she were to resume her relationship with him?

"I won't be staying for dinner," she said coolly. The last thing she wanted was for him to realize how much she hoped that what he'd said would prove true. "I'm going to leave . . . as soon as . . ." Her voice lacked real determination.

"Oh, I don't think you'll be leaving just yet. Remember I've still got your car keys. And that towel you're hugging so fiercely belongs to me."

"You . . ."

"It's nearly nine-fifteen. I know you're hungry."

What was the use? He always had his way with her. "I'll stay."

"That was easy." Blue eyes flashed with triumph. "Sometimes you can be very difficult to persuade." He laughed jauntily then, and threw her her clothes. "There's an ironing board in the utility room you can use."

Kit blew her hair dry with the hair dryer Phyllis kept at Ted's for Missy. She'd pressed her red dress so that it looked almost as fresh as when she'd put it on earlier in the evening.

She switched off the hair dryer. Piano music—low and melodic—was drifting into Ted's bedroom. She heard Ted—brisk and purposeful—moving about in the kitchen. The scent of a charcoal fire was in the air.

She began to brush her hair. Unconsciously she began singing the lyrics of the lovesong the pianist played on the record. Then she caught herself and stilled the brush in mid-air. She was singing—and she only did that when she was very happy.

Slowly, carefully she placed the brush on the cambrian marble counter. She hadn't been this happy for a long time. And it was all because it seemed Fate had turned back a page of time. Rodney was out of her life. She was with Ted, and it seemed to her they were young and in love and planning to be married.

Oh, if only . . . if only . . . things were as wonderful as they seemed. She heard the crisp sounds of Ted's knock on the door. "Kit, are you ready for me to put the steaks on?"

She heard her own voice, a stranger's, call gaily, "Yes, I'll be right out."

They ate out on the terrace beneath a canopy of stars. Two candles in hurricane lamps glimmered from the center of the table. The moon was high and the bay was soft silver ripples. But Kit was so aware of the tall, dark man who sat opposite her, she scarcely noticed the beauty around her. Being with him—as if she belonged with him—was almost too wonderful to believe.

Dinner was superb. Ted cooked—as he did all things—well. The meal was simple: romaine lettuce sprinkled with toasted sesame seeds, finely grated Swiss cheese, and Italian dressing; sauteed mushrooms; fresh green beans garnished with sliced water chestnuts; Texas toast, and steak. And of course he'd remembered her favorite wine.

Throughout the meal Ted was attentive. He acted to perfection the part of ardent suitor. Kit had to work very hard to keep her guard up. At last she asked the question foremost on her mind.

"You said if I stayed for dinner we would discuss your reason for wanting to marry me."

"Suppose I said I had only one reason—that life without you these past five years has been empty."

She caught a strangely husky note in his deep voice, and she almost believed him—because she wanted to so much. She steeled herself against the sincerity of his manner.

"I wouldn't believe you," she said harshly. "Remember I'm not the naive little girl you knew five years ago. I've learned a few things about life. You married Letitia. You have Missy . . ."

"Still, my life is incomplete without . . . you . . . without a wife."

"I don't believe you," she repeated. She was afraid to show how desperately she hoped he cared something for her. "Remember you have already proved your point tonight—about how susceptible I am where you are concerned. You think you can persuade me to believe anything because I . . . I . . ." She'd been dangerously close to say that she loved him.

"Because you what?" He seized her wrist, and when she didn't answer him his fingers tightened until she cried out. "Because you what?"

His eyes were fastened on her face with an intensity that alarmed her. She was afraid he would see her love for him.

"Because . . . I . . . I'm such a . . . because you think I'm such a little fool."

He released her abruptly as if in disgust.

"Is that really what you think?"

"Yes."

"Then you're right! You are a little fool! That's not what I think at all! You used to understand me so well. What's happened to us, Kit?"

"Five years," she said bitterly. "Five long, empty years."

"Empty? Were they empty for you too?" He no longer sounded so angry.

"No! I don't know why I said that. It's just that you confuse me."

"I don't mean to."

"You still haven't told me your reason for wanting to marry me," she persisted stubbornly.

She felt, without seeing, because his face was in the shadows, his gaze linger upon her features. She knew that her expression was tight and guarded. He must never, never know what she felt for him. At last he answered her.

"Well, suppose I said I need a wife to look after me. I'm tired of living alone . . . and then my bookkeeper just quit at the store." He spoke evenly, as if her were interviewing her for a prospective job instead of telling her why he wished to marry her.

"Surely you could hire someone to replace her."

"Not someone with your mind for numbers. I have accounting problems with my ranch and construction company as well."

"Your ranch and your construction company?"

"Yes, your poor boy's made good. But we won't go into that because I wouldn't want to think you were marrying me for my money."

"I would never marry anyone for money!" she flared.

"Wouldn't you?"

She remembered he'd accused her of marrying Rodney for that reason.

"We were discussing your reasons for wanting to marry me," she replied coldly.

"So we were. There's Missy. She needs a mother."

"You have Phyllis to care for her, her own aunt. She'd be much better for her than I would."

"I don't think so."

"Phyllis only lives next door. Looks like the perfect arrangement."

"Then looks are deceiving. Like you, I thought it would be perfect for all of us at first. Phyllis and I have a good relationship with one another. I bought the two townhouses side by side. The second townhouse was to be an investment as well as a convenient place for Phyllis to live and see after Missy. She pays a nominal rent. I thought I could help her get on her feet financially. She's had some problems the past few years. Well, things went along all right for a while, but then it became apparent that Phyllis spoils Missy. You saw what happened tonight."

"So you want to marry me for your own convenience. You need a wife and someone to look after your child. You've said you want me physically, but you haven't mentioned love. I don't suppose that in a 'marriage of convenience' love matters. I do want to make it clear, though, that I'm no more in love with you than you are with me." Her pride drove her to say that last.

He pushed his chair back from the table and stood up, his muscular body rigid with tension. When he spoke his voice was hard.

"I want to marry you, Kit, if you'll have me. Apparently we've lost the ability to trust and understand one another. I'll let you draw your own conclusions as to what my motives are."

He turned and left her then. She heard the sliding glass door slam shut behind him.

For a long time she stared miserably out onto the glistening bay. The scent of salt spray and jasmine filled the air.

She wanted him. She loved him. She would marry
him. She knew she would be behaving foolishly to do so,
but she couldn't stop herself. Without him she would
always be unhappy. If she married him there was a
chance—however remote—he might come to love her.

She heard his movements in the townhouse and
turned to observe him. He'd poured himself another
glass of wine. She saw him bend and turn up the stereo.
Again he was playing the saxophone music he'd played
the night they'd made love.

She went to the glass door and pushed it open. The
music was vibrant and soothing like warm liquid
passion filling the room.

"Have you made your decision yet?" he asked
quietly.

"Yes. I'll marry you . . . on one condition."

He swept her into his arms and before she could even
attempt to resist, he kissed her. Slipping his arm around
her waist, he drew her across the room. He opened the
drawer of a cabinet and pulled out a tiny velvet box.

"I think it's time we made it official," he said.

He handed her the velvet box. Slowly she opened it.
She gasped. An enormous American-cut diamond—at
least two carats—set in a simple setting of yellow gold
flickered in the dim light. Slowly, carefully she removed
it, and he slipped it onto her finger.

"Ted . . . Ted . . . it's lovely," she murmured.

He was staring deeply into her eyes, his expression
unfathomable. She fingered the ring in shy delight.

Impulsively she sprang onto her tiptoes and threw
her arms round his neck and hugged him. Her fingers
were clasped together at the back of his neck, and he
brought his face down to hers. She kissed him lightly on
the cheek. She had meant only to embrace him
affectionately. She had not anticipated his response.

His great hand moved behind her head, forcing her face to slant against his. His mouth covered her lips in a long, searing, demanding kiss. She could feel the fiercely rapid thudding of his heart against her breast. She felt the heaviness of his cast around her back as he crushed the slender curves of her soft body against the threatening hardness of his. She gasped weakly, and she felt his breathing quicken. She heard him groan.

She was aware of his fingers moving downward from her neck to the zipper at the back of her sundress. Deftly he parted the zipper and the dress was slipping from her shoulders. She felt the warmth of his hand moving across her flesh. And as always his nearness, his desire for her, and his touch produced a wild answering thrill in her. Her whole consciousness was stimulated by the taste, the feel, the smell of him.

She was kissing him with a passion that matched his own. She felt a mad impatience to belong to him completely. He was pulling her across the room and drawing her down onto the sofa. His kisses became deeper, longer; the caressing touch of his fingers—intimate fire. She was breathless with longing for him, shivering gently with ecstasy.

His mouth traced downward from her lips to her earlobes. She was moaning softly as she lay limply beneath him. She felt the blistering heat of his lips as he gently·kissed the tips of her breasts. Her fingers were intertwined in his auburn hair and she held him to her fiercely so that he would go on kissing her there forever and ever.

His voice was a low murmur. "My darling, Kit. You're all I can think about, all I want. Let me make love to you now."

His hand moved slowly downward.

The deep husky sound of the saxophone enveloped

them. *The same sound as before. Before—when he'd almost made love to her and—before she'd lost him!*

The grip of her fingers in his hair slowly weakened. The memory of his treachery was dampening—like throwing cold water onto fire. While some of the heat of that fire may remain, the flames go out.

Oh no! No! No! She must find a way to stop him before it was too late, and she was lost. She forced herself to break away and because that was the last thing he expected, it was easy to do.

"I said I'd marry you on one condition," she said thickly. Her fingers shook as she brushed her hair back from her face.

"What? What in hell are you talking about?"

"I'll marry you if you promise me you won't touch me. Do you understand? I don't want you to make love to me—ever."

"Kit . . ."

"I mean it. Don't come near me. Not tonight . . . or ever."

"Kit, I don't want to promise that. I want you. I lo . . ."

"Don't say it! You'll say anything to a girl to make her give in to you. Surely I should know that by now." He was staring at her as if he couldn't believe what she was saying. "Is that understood? If we marry, you must promise not to touch me. Not even to kiss me. The only reason I'm considering marrying you is to save my reputation—which will be in shreds because of you!" When he said nothing: "I won't marry you if you don't."

His eyes hardened; his mouth twisted. Slowly he sat up on the sofa. He pulled the edges of his shirt together and began to laboriously button them with his left hand. When he spoke his voice was deep and cold.

"I see Kit, you're set on being a fool. You seem determined to ruin things between us again."

Her voice was equally cold. "Will you promise?"

"Yes."

He arose from the sofa and slipped his belt through the loops of his dungarees. She was terribly aware of him as a man—of his height as he stood over her, the breadth of his shoulders, his muscles tapering to his narrow waist, the purposeful movements of his fingers at his belt buckle—those same fingers that could touch her gently and make her flesh burn like fire.

He was at the door. She heard something jingle faintly and watched as he tossed her keys onto the carpet at her feet.

Then he pulled the door open, and stepped out into the night. He slammed it behind him, and she was left alone.

She had won! He'd given her his word. But why did her victory feel so hollow?

Chapter Seven

The day of the wedding dawned clear and bright. Kit was in her room waiting to make her appearance. She wore a gown of ivory lace that hugged the curves of her body more provocatively than a wedding gown should. Never had her waist looked tinier. The neckline was low and scalloped.

More than a month had elapsed since the night Ted had proposed. She had not seen much of him since that evening. He had been out of town for two weeks on business at his ranch. She had been busy with preparations for the wedding. When she had seen him he had been coolly polite. He had kept to their bargain—he had not touched her.

Why was he marrying her? He had agreed to forego the physical side of marriage and his recent lack of attentiveness was beginning to make her wonder if he was really all that attracted to her anyway. Could such a marriage work? Was she a fool to rush into it? Her rational mind told her that she was, but love wasn't rational. And she loved him.

Kit had wanted a small wedding after the disaster of the first one, but the small garden wedding had mushroomed into an enormous affair.

Kit shakily fingered the rope of pears at her throat—Ted's wedding gift to her—as she studied the milling crowd beneath her balcony. She would have to go down soon. An enormous yellow and white striped party tent—bigger even than the one they'd rented a month ago—stood in readiness for the wedding and reception to follow. Her mother had hired a band at the last minute.

A small wedding! Kit laughed nervously at the thought. Although they'd sent invitations only to family, in the past month her sociable mother had invited everyone she'd talked to on the telephone, everyone she'd run into, however casually.

"I just couldn't leave *them* out, *querida*," she'd explained over and over to her daughter as the guest list grew longer. And when Kit had stormed about the band: "*Querida*, it just wouldn't be a wedding without music. You know how we all love to dance."

Kit had seen to only one detail of the wedding herself. She'd had a small replica of the giant wedding cake made. The smaller cake was chocolate on the inside, and she'd had it made for a certain little girl who loved chocolate.

Anitra came to her room and told her it was time for her to come down.

"Mother, is he . . ." She lowered her voice and whispered in Spanish, the language they used sometimes when they were alone. "Is he here?"

Her mother reassured her in Spanish. "*Sí, querida.*

107

He has been here from the first. He is so anxious to marry you. And, oh, he is so handsome today. Dressed in dark blue. His suit is the color of those darker rings around his eyes. He has such beautiful eyes. So blue. So expressive. I have watched them fill with love when he looks at you."

Kit thought her mother was too effusive about Ted's love for her, but she relaxed a bit. At least—this time—she wasn't going to be jilted.

They were married.

The band was playing a Spanish polka, and Ted was claiming her for his partner. In spite of his cast, he held her tightly and moved with that flowing grace that was characteristic of him.

"And so now, Kit, you are mine."

"In name only."

"You have a strange idea of marriage."

"You promised to go along with it."

"And for a month, I've kept my promise. But I'm growing weary of that promise, aren't you? Remember we are married now."

The music was ending, and before she could answer, Steve was asking her for the next dance.

"Kit, I'm happy for you today," her brother said as he whirled Kit across the dance floor beneath the tent.

Kit looked past Steve and noticed that Ted was dancing with Phyllis. Phyllis looked unhappy although she was beautiful in a gown of blue threaded with wisps of gold. Ted's expression was tender with concern as he bent his head low and talked to her. Suddenly Phyllis broke from his arms and ran across the lawn as if she were desperate to get away from the wedding activities. Ted was right behind her. Kit watched miserably as he caught up with her, and seized her by the hand. He led

108

Phyllis—still holding her by the hand—away from the crowd toward the water.

The music stopped and Kit was hardly aware that it did so. All she could think of was Ted—with Phyllis. Why didn't he return? Where had they gone? What was their relationship? Was he in love with her? Was she in love with him?

Steve led his sister from the dance floor, and her father, smiling proudly, joined them and began discussing the next yacht series. But Kit wasn't listening to them; she was aware only of Ted's lengthening absence from the wedding festivities.

Another Spanish song was played and then a western song. Kit found herself only half listening to those who spoke to her. Her gaze kept straying toward the lawn stretching toward the seawall that was hidden from her view by a clump of oleander and olive trees. Phyllis and Ted still had not returned.

At last her mother came and told her that the photographer wished to take a few more pictures of her and Ted together.

Kit wandered across the lawn in search of Ted and Phyllis. At first she could not find them because the foliage at that end of the estate was dense. Her father had had it planted for privacy.

She heard them before she saw them. Their voices were clear and distinct like sounds carried across water.

Phyllis was talking in a tear-choked voice. "You'll never make me understand why you're marrying her. You don't love her! You couldn't!"

Not wanting to hear another word, Kit called to them loudly. She gave Phyllis a moment to compose herself before she joined them.

"The photographer wants to take more pictures,"

she said simply, feeling miserable and embarrassed that she had interrupted them.

Ted slipped his good arm through hers. He seemed genuinely glad to see her—almost relieved. "Phyllis is worried about how Missy will react to our marriage," he said in explanation of Phyllis's tear-streaked face. "But she hopes we'll be very happy together." He eyed Phyllis sternly, daring her to object to his explanation. "She wants to keep Missy at her house for a little while—to give her a chance to adjust to our marriage."

Steve was coming across the lawn. "The photographer . . ."

"We're coming," Kit answered.

Steve pulled Ted to one side to ask him something.

Kit turned to Phyllis. "Phyllis," she said gently, "I won't try to take your place with Missy. I hope you know that. But I do intend to give her all the love I can possibly . . ."

Phyllis didn't wait for her to finish. "You don't fool me for a minute, Kit Jackson! You couldn't care less about Missy! And you are the last person Letitia would have wanted raising her child. I know you've wanted Ted for a long time. Letitia told me how you tried to take him away from her!"

"Phyllis, that's not true."

"You're just a spoiled rich girl who thinks she can have anything or anyone she wants. You'll ruin Ted's life and Missy's too . . . He deserves a different kind of woman. A woman more like . . ."

Phyllis never finished what she would have said, for Ted was saying smoothly, "Girls, are you ready?" He took Kit by the arm and led her back to the house.

What would Phyllis have said, had she completed her sentence? Was she in love with Ted herself? Was that it? Did she think Ted loved her in return? Was that why she thought Kit couldn't make him happy?

Kit was beginning to have real doubts about the wisdom of her hasty marriage.

The photographer had a last-minute inspiration.

"Let me get one more picture of you two," he said to the newlyweds. "One of you kissing."

Before she could resist, Ted was pulling her into his arms, crushing her to him. She saw the determination on his face, the glint in his eyes. He smiled down at her triumphantly. She knew he was remembering his promise not to touch her or kiss her. Just as she knew he was going to seize this opportunity to kiss her in spite of that promise. She twisted her face to evade his lips, but he was too quick for her. She felt the warmth and wetness of his open lips cover hers and linger there nibbling slowly, softly, and then insistently until her lips parted as well.

The camera had ceased its mad clicking, and still he kissed her. Still he pressed her slim body against his own. In spite of herself and the circumstances she enjoyed the hard, masculine feel of his body against hers, the intimacy of his lips on hers. Her brain was spinning; she felt dizzy and breathless from his kisses. But he did not release her.

She could almost feel her resistance weakening. As always her need for him betrayed her, and she lifted her arms and circled his neck.

His triumphant chuckle tickling her throat warmly brought her back to reality.

"You see, that promise is as hard for you to keep as it is for me."

She pushed against him, but he held her to him.

The photographer was thanking them. "That's great. Just great!" His camera clicked one final time.

"It certainly is," Ted agreed. He was smiling broadly down at her.

He was laughing then as he held her to him, and so was she. Phyllis and her angry words were forgotten, and Kit was hoping fervently that somehow, someway the two of them could find a way to be happy together.

The festivities were far from over when Ted insisted that they leave. Kit had changed from her wedding gown into a demure three-piece suit that was done in three shades of lavender. Ted tucked her into his low-slung sports car. Anitra, tears of happiness streaming down her face, bent down to kiss Kit. Then Ted was in the car beside her and stepping on the gas pedal. Rice showered them, and cans tied to the rear bumper of their car were clatter on concrete as they sped away into the twilight.

Kit watched the incessant crashing of the waves against the concrete bulkhead beneath her as she waited at Ted's front door for him to return from the car with the rest of her things. She heard his heavy tread as he approached. She watched as he set her suitcases down.

"Isn't it tradition that a groom should take his bride in his arms and carry her over the threshold?" he asked.

"I'm surprised you care for traditions."

"I don't, unless they suit my purpose."

He was staring down at her, his gaze direct and piercing. Then before she could stop him he pulled her to him and held her tightly.

"Kit, this is the beginning of our life together."

"Aren't you forgetting your promise?"

The mere mention of it seemed to enrage him.

"My promise . . . !"

His mouth came down hard upon hers, forcing her lips apart. He kissed her hungrily, passionately, no longer with restraint. Just as she was dizzy from his kisses his lips left hers.

With one movement he was stooping. His left hand traveled over her body, and he grasped her at the knees, lifting her and swinging her onto his left shoulder. He held her there, slung over his shoulder like a heavy sack, as he struggled with his keys and the lock of his front door.

"Put me down!" She kicked at him wildly. "What do you think you're doing?"

"Be quiet! I'm carrying you across the threshold." He was slamming the door and bolting it, forgetting their suitcases and leaving them outside.

"You certainly have a strange way of doing it," she said as he carried her across his living room and into his bedroom.

"And you, my darling, have only yourself to thank for that. Remember if it weren't for you, I wouldn't have a broken arm, and I could carry you properly."

He flung her onto the bed and before she could do anything other than gasp he was on top of her. Her black hair spread in gleaming ripples across his bed. Her black eyes were luminous.

"You are very beautiful, Kit," he said softly. "Very beautiful. And I want you. I want you more than I've ever wanted you. We're married now . . ."

"You promised," she said weakly. She tried to keep her body stiff beneath his.

"I know I did, and I've kept that promise for a month. Do you really want me to keep it now?"

Oh, he was close, too close! She couldn't think! A lock of his thick hair had fallen across his tanned

113

forehead. He was terribly handsome. Just the feel of his hard body covering hers . . . She was so, so vulnerable to his appeal, and he knew it.

With his fingertips he traced and retraced the curve of her ear. She was gasping. He knew, too well, what his touch there did to her.

"Do you?" he repeated his question.

He brought his lips to her throat and kissed the mad pulsebeat there.

She moved underneath him. Slowly she lifted her hands and caressed his rough cheeks. She pulled his face to hers and kissed him tentatively on the lips, and then because she could not stop herself, more passionately.

She should despise herself for her weakness, for giving in so easily, but she couldn't. She was too caught up in the joy of the moment, the joy of his wanting her. And she wanted him; she wanted to belong to him completely—even if he could never be hers in the same way. She knew that being with him would be beautiful, and she would treasure the memory of it always—even if she lost him again.

Suddenly she was thinking of beautiful things: Missy smiling fleetingly, pink flamingos flying low over darkening waves, and wild olive blossoms blooming and blowing in the wind. Were these things less beautiful because of the transient quality of their beauty, or were they all the more precious because they couldn't last?

Life was like that too, wasn't it? Filled with beautiful moments that couldn't endure. She knew she had to surrender herself to the beauty of this moment. Living life to the fullest meant taking risks. She knew she was risking her heart to love him a second time. But if she didn't take the chance, she would have to go on as she had. Anything, even that terrible hurt was preferable to feeling that strange, hollow emptiness that was not being alive at all.

She was aware of his hand moving gently, beneath her chin and down the curve of her neck to rest upon the swell of her breast. He was staring at her in wonder, as if he thought her very beautiful. He was unfastening the tiny buttons of her blouse. He bent his head and with his lips nudged the silken edges of her blouse aside. He was unhooking the bit of lace that was her bra. She felt his lips warm and nuzzling on her flesh once more, finding the ripe softness of her breasts, and kissing them until she was shivering with pleasure.

He helped her to sit up. He was pushing her jacket over her shoulders, helping her slip out of her blouse. His eyes went over her, and the sight of her—her full rounded breasts, the smoothness of her olive skin—inflamed him. He smiled at her tenderly before crushing her to him. Her hair was tumbling about her shoulders and he buried his face in its rich darkness and kissed her on her neck beneath her earlobe. She heard his voice, vibrant with passion, murmuring love words to her.

With shaking fingers she unbuttoned his shirt. Deftly, in spite of his cast, he pulled it off. Then he held her to him for a long moment as if she were very dear to him. She felt the thick hairs of his chest against her breasts, the incredible heat of him.

If only he really loved her, as she loved him, she would have been completely happy. But he only wanted her physically!

Though eyes blurred with desire she watched as he hastily undressed and then undressed her. He was pulling her to him and covering her body with the long length of his. She was trembling and so was he.

"You smell sweet—like flowers," he murmured. His hands gently caressed her body as he kissed her.

Her mind seemed to go blank for a while. She forgot her doubts about him. She was aware only of her driving need for him. His kisses became more urgent; his body moved purposefully, pliant to hers, responsive to her slightest movement. His touch was like fire and ice. One moment her flesh seemed to burn and the next she was shivering. He was embracing her tightly, and for one long moment, it seemed to her that they were one—not only physically but emotionally and spiritually.

The tension drained from them, and still he did not move from her. He held her, cradling her in his arms.

Time passed. Except for a sprinkle of lights across the bay all was blackness and silence outside. He was holding her still, as if he couldn't bear to let her go. And strangely she felt even closer to him afterward than she had when he'd made love to her.

The terrible thought came to her. What would happen if she lost him now . . . after this wonderful moment of shared closeness. How could she bear it?

His lips sought hers again and he kissed her gently as if he truly loved her. And suddenly, for no reason at all, she was weeping. He kissed her eyelids that were wet with tears and her cheeks that were also tear-wet.

He spoke softly. "Why are you crying?"

"Because . . . because . . ." In that moment she could do nothing but be honest. "Because—before—I lost you."

She felt his muscles tense. "You didn't lose me, you left me. Remember?" he said in a voice that was now tinged with bitterness.

He pulled away from her. The closeness that had existed between them was gone. In the darkness she was aware of him fumbling for his clothes and hastily dressing. He left the bedroom and went into the living room.

Why did the mention of the past always anger him? She lay back, tears smarting in the back of her eyes. After a while she drifted into an uneasy sleep.

An hour later the phone rang. Although Ted answered the extension in the living room before it rang twice, Kit woke up. Who could have called them on their wedding night? She felt increasingly uneasy when she heard the front door click softly shut. Ted had gone out without bothering to come in and explain to her where he was going.

While he was gone she bathed and dressed in a pair of tan slacks and a green silk blouse. An hour passed and he didn't return. At last she decided to go out and see if he'd taken the car.

She found his car where they'd parked it earlier. He was on foot unless someone had come by for him.

She decided to search the beach. She stepped from the pebbled walk onto the lawn that sloped downward toward the seawall.

Suddenly she saw him. He was standing on the concrete bulkhead, holding a woman in his arms. Phyllis!

Involuntarily Kit stepped deeper into the shadows.

Ted's head was bent over Phyllis's, and he seemed to be talking earnestly to her. But, because of the rhythmic lapping and splashing of the waves against the bulkhead, Kit could not hear what he was saying.

As she watched them she felt frozen—in a state of stunned shock. Phyllis . . . and Ted. . . . Ted had made love to her and then gone to Phyllis. It seemed to her that tonight was a bitter repetition of the past.

Somehow she managed to get back to the townhouse. She sat down on the couch. She felt cold like ice—cold to the marrow of her bones. Her stomach was queasy. All of the warmth she'd felt for him when he'd made love to her was gone and in its place was a terrible, hollow coldness.

Why had she married him? Why hadn't she seen something like this would happen? He hadn't changed.

Ted came in a few minutes later. His face looked tense and strained. Doubtless he was dreading returning to his wife. Was he regretting their hasty marriage as she was?

"Where did you go?" she asked quietly.

He hesitated only a second. "For a walk. It's a beautiful night."

"Did you run into anyone out there?"

Again he hesitated. Evasively: "I pretty much had the place to myself."

His half-truth was incriminating. Clearly he had no desire to tell her he'd met Phyllis. If their meeting had been innocent, wouldn't he have told her?

He came to the couch, and when he sat down beside her, she shuddered. He pulled her to him, and at first, he didn't notice that she was wooden in his arms.

His lips seemed to burn her flesh. She tried to pull away, but he caught her to him fiercely. His mouth came down hard on hers. What was the use of fighting him? She let her lips remain cool and passive beneath his.

He drew back. "What's wrong, Kit?"

"Everything," she wanted to say, but she said nothing. If she mentioned Phyllis, he would probably put together some half-baked explanation that wouldn't satisfy her anyway. Then they would argue, and what would that accomplish? There was no way she could make him be faithful to her, if he didn't choose to be. She wasn't his jailer.

"Nothing," she said in a small, tight voice.

"I can see by the look on your face that something's wrong."

If she didn't know better she would think he was genuinely concerned. She marveled at his duplicity.

"I'm just tired, that's all. And if you don't mind, I think I'll go on to bed."

"I was hoping we could have dinner together."

"You'll have to count me out."

"Kit, this is our wedding night."

"Believe me, unlike you, I haven't forgotten it for a minute." With that she arose from the couch, and would have marched to the bedroom had he not jumped up and grabbed her.

"Now what in the world is that supposed to mean?"

"I don't think I need to spell it out. Figure it out for yourself."

She left him then, and went into the bedroom. He made no attempt to follow her. A few minutes later she heard the front door shut and she knew he had gone out.

She cried herself to sleep wondering if he'd gone to Phyllis.

The next morning she wakened to the sound of Ted in the kitchen, to the smell of eggs and bacon and biscuits cooking. She was about to get up when he entered the room, a cup of coffee in his hand. "Feeling better?" he asked.

Her heart flip flopped crazily at the warmth in his voice. He was smiling down at her, a smoldering light burning in his blue eyes at the vision of her in his bed.

"Yes," she murmured, averting his gaze. Just the sight of him this morning—handsomely masculine—and she felt shyly nervous. She realized how vulnerable she was to his appeal. He had only to smile to disarm her.

"Good." He leaned down and brushed her forehead quickly with his lips. She knew she had only to respond and she would feel the wondrous rapture of his lips on hers, of his arms circling her in a passionate embrace. But the inner demon of doubt still possessed her. She endured his kiss stiffly, and he withdrew his lips. He handed her the cup of coffee. He smiled at her again; this time his smile showed the strain of control. "Don't get up. This morning I'm going to serve you breakfast in bed to make up to you for not taking you on a honeymoon."

"I never expected a honeymoon."

"You're very understanding. I will take you on a trip as soon as I can get away from the business. That's one of the penalties of being in business for yourself—you can't always leave when you want to. Right now I'm developing a tract of land on the Intercoastal Canal near Aransas Pass for an oil company. We're dredging a canal and building docks. I just can't leave in the middle of it. This is our big season. We have several cattle sales coming up and those mean tent rentals and table and chair rentals."

"From what you say, I gather your businesses are doing well?" Gingerly she sipped the steaming coffee. She felt much more relaxed with him than when he'd first come into the room. He'd expertly manuevered their conversation onto safe ground.

"They are. When other areas of my life did not work out, I put all my energy into them." His face had darkened. "But now . . . that I have you, I'll want to spend more time at home." Again the intimate tone of his voice sent her pulse beats tripping.

He did not pursue the subject further. Instead he returned to the kitchen and left her to finish her coffee.

They spent the rest of the day alone together, and she almost succeeded in pushing Phyllis from her mind.

That afternoon he took her to the shipyard where *Wild Lady* was in dry dock for repairs. Ted told her he'd hired professionals to do most of the work because he wanted her to be ready for the next yacht series.

"This time, with you crewing for me instead of for your father, I won't have any trouble beating him. I won't have to worry about someone running into me," he teased.

That afternoon he told her things about himself she'd never known before. He told her of the first ten years of his life, the years he'd spent in a foster home before he was adopted. He told her how he'd longed to have a family like hers, how he'd longed for security.

"At Christmas rich people used to send us baskets of food and cheap little presents so our Christmas wouldn't be quite so bleak at the foster home," he said. "Sometimes we would even get to ride down Ocean Drive to see the Christmas lights as a special treat. We would pass by some of the homes that belonged to the people who so carelessly made those donations. Kit, I don't know if you can understand what it is to have nothing . . . and to want so much." His voice caught with remembered bitterness.

"I've made a lot of money, Kit. It took a lot of money before I learned it wasn't just money I wanted. It was love and security as well. Happiness. I was starved for it." He set the tool he'd been working with down. He was reaching for her and pulling her into his arms. He held her close. "There was a time when I wanted all

121

those things so much I almost hated anyone who had them. Having Missy helped. I didn't want her to grow up with all the twisted feelings I had. And now that I have you to help me raise her, I know she'll grow up taking for granted all the things I missed. She's going to love you—and soon. And in time we'll have children of our own . . ."

If only Kit hadn't known about Phyllis, the afternoon would have been idyllic. The knowledge touched everything with a strange bittersweetness.

Ted took her to dinner at an elegant restaurant overlooking the bay. The dining room was softly aglow with candle light; beneath them the bay like a sheet of smooth glass reflected the night beauty of the city and its lights. Throughout dinner he gripped her hand as if he could not bear to sit through the meal without touching her.

When they returned home he immediately drew her to the bedroom and into his arms. She tried to push away from him, saying she was tired. He paid no attention to her protests.

"I can't let a wife of mine fall into bad habits," he teased, his gaze possessively roaming over her face. She was acutely aware of his fingers in her hair, of his nearness, of the warmness flowing like a treacherous flood through her. "Tomorrow night it will be a head-ache or some other bit of nonsense. When all the time you want me as much as I want you."

"Oh, you're impossibly conceited," she whispered in a shaky voice that betrayed all too clearly she was not immune to his appeal. "You think you can have any woman." She was thinking achingly again of Phyllis, of him holding her close to him in his arms.

"We're not talking about any woman. We're talking about you. It's you I want—you I intend to have. Have you forgotten that you belong to me? That you're my wife?"

She struggled in earnest, but he was stronger, and more determined. His mouth closed over hers in a long kiss. And as always, her will to fight him drained from her.

He bent her backwards and she felt the bed beneath her, and his body on top of hers. Then she was aware of nothing but the swirling mad bliss of his touch, the ecstasy of his embrace as the fire of their passionate desire leaped into roaring flame.

She was lost, as he'd known she would be.

His mouth followed the curve of her chin to the hollow of her throat. Slowly he undressed her. She felt the hard warmth of his hands at her bare waist, pulling her body against his, molding her to his length.

Her own fingers combed the thick auburn mane that was his hair. Her lips found his once more in an ardent, drugging kiss. . . .

When it was over, he fell asleep almost at once, but she lay awake remembering the thrill of his touch, the heat of his kisses. He'd clasped her to him, his fingers pressing against her spine as if she'd belonged to him utterly. She'd felt hot like an overbright star—sparkling with light, flaming with glory.

When it was like that between them she found it difficult to believe he could love another woman as he did her. She could not doubt his passion.

Still, the vision of him holding Phyllis in his arms was indelibly stamped on her brain.

Weren't men different than women? They didn't

always love the women they desired. But she loved him! Fiercely!

Yet the thought that he might love Phyllis was tearing her to pieces. She couldn't endure marriage to a man—even Ted—if he wasn't faithful.

What was she going to do?

Chapter Eight

Kit stirred drowsily, awakening. The bright glare of morning sunlight was slanting through the partially opened floor-to-ceiling draperies. Outside she saw an expanse of summer sky—brilliant blue. The bay was undulating green glitter. Then the man beside her stretched sleepily. She felt the hard warmth of his fingers move across the bare flesh of her stomach as he moved nearer and snuggled against her.

She stared down at his face, partially concealed by the tumbled sheets. Red highlights glinted in his tousled hair. Sleep had smoothed the lines from his face, and his gentle expression was strangely at variance with his virile, rugged features. He pressed his lips lightly to her shoulder, and where his lips touched her, her skin tingled.

She almost hated him because she loved him so much. He was capable of hurting her as no other man could. Effortlessly he aroused her deepest emotions; carelessly he disregarded her for another woman. He had done it in the past, and she was almost positive he was doing it in the present.

He had talked of learning from past mistakes, of changing. She was beginning to realize, he hadn't meant a word he'd said.

The telephone rang, and Ted answered it. Kit could tell by the low, intimate tone he used as well as by the fact he was discussing Missy that the caller was Phyllis.

To Kit's horror she heard him invite the other girl and Missy to dinner that evening.

When he hung up the phone, he rolled over and kissed Kit leisurely on the throat.

She tried to spring away, but he was holding her down.

"I think we overslept," she said coldly.

"Did we?" His voice was lazy. "Surely the world expects that of newlyweds."

His lips were hot and searching, and her own senses were quickening, ready to drag her into the powerful undercurrent of his desire. In another minute he would be making love to her. Longing quivered through her like fire tongues flicking as she forced herself to twist away from him.

"It's almost seven thirty," she said tautly. "Aren't you supposed to be at work by eight?" She pulled the covers over her rigid body.

This time he heard the impatience in her voice; he sensed the tension in her.

"Don't tell me you're going to start nagging me this early in our marriage," he replied lightly. "The store opens at eight, but I own it, remember? I don't have to be there until I get there."

He was bending over her to kiss her again, and a sigh

126

shuddered from her lips. She shrank from him. She mustn't, she simply mustn't let him! He didn't love her, he only wanted to use her. She pushed him away.

He sat up, the sheets falling from him and exposing his furred, muscular chest. He was staring down at her quizzically as if he were trying to understand her mood. Then his expression hardened. He reached for his quartz watch and clipped it around his wrist. She knew he'd decided to curb his desire because that was what he thought she wanted. Fleetingly a pang of disappointment, keen and sharp like a knife's edge, winged through her. She'd denied them both the rapture of physical love, and it hurt. He turned back to her, and when he spoke his tone was harsh.

"Well, if I have to get up, so do you, madame. It's time you learned there's more to being a wife than being a bedmate." He raked his eyes over her until she blushed. "You're so anxious to see me off to work— well, I'm just as anxious for you to get into the kitchen and fix my breakfast. I have a long day ahead of me, and I don't intend to face it on an empty stomach." When she made no move to follow his instructions: "Or do you intend to remain the spoiled little rich girl who can't even boil an egg?" he finished.

"I . . . I . . ." She was about to say that she couldn't possibly cook his breakfast because she didn't know how. His blue eyes were on her face, boldly challenging her as he waited for her to answer. "Of course I can cook!" she cried out. "What do you want to eat?"

"Well, I'll be thoughtful and keep in simple. How about three boiled eggs, toast, bacon, and coffee— black. You should be able to manage that." The faintly taunting tone of his voice implied that he very much doubted she could.

Of course she could manage that! Housewives all

over the country did it for large families. Why couldn't she?

When she heard the sound of water streaming in the shower, and of him whistling safely inside it, she slipped from the bed and into a robe. She went into the kitchen and began the task of preparing his breakfast.

Nothing is ever as easy to do as it seems. The eggs broke as they boiled and became knotty, rubbery stretches of white in the turbulent water. How long did one boil eggs anyway?

She forgot the toast. She was removing it smoking from the toaster when Ted, stuffing his shirt into his trousers, entered the kitchen.

"I thought I smelled breakfast."

"Don't tease me," she said miserably. "I burned your toast. Those eggs look like rubber."

"What happened to the bacon?"

"Oh! I forgot about it completely." She was pulling the frying pan out of the cupboard. "It will only take a minute."

"Never mind."

Tears of frustration were filling her eyes.

"Brides are supposed to burn toast and cook rubbery eggs," he said gently in low-pitched tones.

Then before she had time to resist, he was pulling her into his arms and kissing her. Her heart leapt with alarm at his touch. When she pushed him away, he frowned but said nothing.

"And new husbands are supposed to eat what their brides cook," she answered with flashing temper.

He ran tap water into his coffee and carried his cup to the table. He ate his breakfast in silence. When he finished he said, "I'll do the dishes while you get ready for work."

"Work?"

"You don't think I'm going to have a wife lying around the house when she could be useful to me. I'm sure your father let you lounge around to your heart's content between trips to Europe, but you're married to me now and I'm not nearly so rich as he. I need your help in the business. I told you my bookkeeper quit, and I'm falling behind on my books. I think it's high time you put that college education of yours to work."

At his words her black eyes sparked with fury, but again he was challenging her. And she could not refuse him.

"All right. I'll be ready in a few minutes," she replied tightly, and went to the bedroom to dress.

When she returned, dressed stylishly in apricot Qiana, fifteen minutes later she found Ted reading the paper.

"Well, I'm ready," she said coldly.

His voice went equally cold. "Good." He arose and opened the door for her. They stepped out into the sunshine.

As they drove to the store, he said, "I think you heard me invite Phyllis to dinner tonight. We haven't seen Missy since our wedding, and I want her to feel that she's a part of our lives."

"You invited them without asking me."

"I'm asking you now. If you want to do something different tonight I can call Phyllis and cancel. She's very understanding."

"I'm sure you think she is," Kit said sarcastically.

"What is that supposed to mean?"

"Nothing."

"I didn't like the tone of your voice."

"Sorry. Maybe I don't like the situation."

"What in heaven's name are you talking about now?"

He drove the car into the parking lot of his store and stepped on the brakes. She was about to get out, when his large brown hand wrapped around hers.

"Not so fast," he said, his voice ominously soft. "You're not going anywhere until we get this cleared up. You've been acting strangely all morning and I want to know why."

A quick sideways glance on her part, and she saw the hardened set of his jawline and the angry fire of his eyes. She was going to have to tell him something, but, she certainly didn't feel up to discussing Phyllis with him this morning. The hurt went too deep. She was convinced he would invent a lie to explain his involvement with his sister-in-law. Her mind searched desperately for something to divert him.

"Maybe I don't appreciate you asking them to eat dinner . . . when . . . you know what a terrible cook I am. Have you forgotten what I did to breakfast? I couldn't possibly cook a meal if I can't boil an egg. We would all die of embarrassment . . . if my cooking didn't kill us first. . . ."

He was looking at her oddly. "Are you sure that's what's bothering you?" His look held a silent warning that she be truthful. "You look awfully worried . . ."

"Of course that's what's bothering me . . ." She avoided his gaze.

The tension in his grip relaxed.

"Then you have nothing to worry about. Tonight I'll do the cooking."

Ted's store was a centrally located modern brick building on a busy thoroughfare. It had large plate glass windows to show off his equipment and party rental items. He led her through the store to a newly remodeled office. It was done in blues—her favorite shades. The desk was gleaming white. The wallpaper was delightful. Blue twists, shells, were arranged on silver foil.

"Ted, it's beautiful." Her eyes shone with delight.

"I hoped you'd like it," he said. There was an answering light in his eyes as they shared a quick moment of mutual joy. Involuntarily she felt herself responding to him. "I had it remodeled just for you. Phyllis helped me."

"Phyllis?"

"You knew she works out of an interior design studio nearby, didn't you? She did my townhouse too. I told her your favorite colors."

"I didn't realize . . ." she was murmuring.

The mention of Phyllis spoiled her happiness in the lovely office. Why did he bother pretending he'd done all this for her? No doubt he'd relished the excuse to be with Phyllis.

"I bought you a new calculator," he was saying, "and a small computer. I thought when you organize my books we'd put them on the computer. I'll teach you how to operate it. That will give us something to do in the evenings when we're not doing something else. . . . I know how you love to play with numbers." Through the thick sweep of her black lashes, she glanced quickly up at his lean, towering profile. His eyes were gleaming as he looked down at her. It was all too easy to read his mind, and she stepped back nervously. "Your passion for numbers is only exceeded by your passion for . . ."

"Stop it!" she said irritably. "I thought you were going to show me your books."

"So I was."

Ted showed her around the store, and she marveled at how well-run it was. If only the books were as orderly as the rest of his business. He was using an intricate hand system for his books that was not only time consuming but gave little information. No wonder the bookkeeper had quit.

He showed her his office and his files. When she knew where all the information she might need was located, he left her sitting at her desk poring over a stack of ledgers, his check book, bank statements, and day sheets that were piled high on top of it. She became so absorbed in her work that she scarcely noticed when he kissed her cheek and said good-bye as he left shortly before noon, saying he had an appointment with his doctor to have his cast removed.

Two hours passed and when he did not return she began to wonder where he was.

Suddenly her inner doubts about him attacked with renewed force. He could be with Phyllis. Discreetly lunching in some out-of-the-way, romantic restaurant. With trembling fingers she laid her pencil on top of one of her ledgers.

He'd said he had a doctor's appointment. Why couldn't she simply trust him as a wife should trust her husband?

The vision—graphic and hurtful—of him holding Phyllis in his arms returned. Then she remembered the old hurt when she'd called him all those years ago and Letitia smugly, triumphantly had answered the phone. He hadn't changed. Why had she ever thought he could.

All at once—perhaps because it was nearly two o'clock and she hadn't eaten since breakfast—she felt weakly tearful. Or perhaps it was the strain of having controlled her feelings ever since she'd seen him on the beach with Phyllis.

She sought for control of her emotions and failed.

Bursting into tears, she buried her face in her hands and sobbed.

She should have known where marriage to him would lead. She should have been wiser and prevented this new pain.

A knock sounded faintly at her door, and she looked up. The last thing she needed was a visitor now. Her pain was private, not something she wanted to share with anyone.

The knock sounded again, and she wiped at her eyes. "J–just a minute."

Before she had a chance to compose herself, Rodney pushed the door open. "Kit? I see Bradley's got you up at his salt mine."

She looked up, unpleasantly startled that it was he, and managed a terse, "Hi, Rodney."

His back was to her as he pushed the door closed. He still hadn't noticed anything was wrong. With tear-wet palms she brushed at her eyes once more.

"Bradley here? I needed to discuss the terms regarding the tents and other items I want to rent for my cattle sale."

"I'm sorry, but he's out," she said in quick dismissal.

"Well, I sure need to talk to him. Haven't got all day." Rodney paced impatiently; she saw he was as uncomfortable in her presence as she was in his. Suddenly he blurted, "Hey, are you okay? Your eyes are all red. . . . Have you . . ."

She interrupted him quickly. Rodney was the last person she would confide her troubles to. "I–I must have gotten some dust in my eyes. These ledgers have been up there for months." She pointed upward to the top of the filing cabinet. She was a poor liar and was sure he wouldn't be fooled for a minute. To her surprise, he believed her.

Swiftly he leaned over her desk, and just as swiftly she cringed away from his inspecting gaze. "Maybe I should have a look," he said. "They're really red." Before she could stop him he tilted her face upward and touched one of her eyelids with a roughened fingertip. His face hovered just inches from hers. "There! Got it!" he exclaimed triumphantly. "It wasn't dust. An eyelash. That's all."

It was then that Ted, tense because he was running late, burst into the office without bothering to knock. At the sight of Rodney leaning over Kit he stopped abruptly in mid-step.

"What are you doing here, Starr? And why is the door closed?"

"I was waiting for you—to discuss terms for the cattle sale rental." Rodney moved away from Kit and faced Bradley.

"Then come into my office and we can discuss them," Ted said in a cold, low voice.

The two men departed. Half an hour later Ted buzzed Kit on the intercom.

"I want to see you in my office at once," he ordered.

When she entered his office, he arose and pulled out a chair for her.

"Rodney's gone?" she asked, avoiding his searing gaze because it made her feel oddly uncomfortable.

"Obviously."

"Did you get the rental?" she asked nervously.

"Of course."

His abrupt manner made her feel even more nervous. "Well, I'm glad of that," she said, faltering. "What was it you wanted to see me about?" When he didn't answer, she looked up and into eyes that were so dark with fury she scarcely knew him. His expression was cold and hard.

"I want you to explain that touching little scene I broke up in your office."

His accusing scrutiny of her features made her feel defiant. "Nothing happened that requires an explanation," she said stiffly.

"You were in his arms."

"I was not! I . . ." She was about to say, "I was crying . . . and Rodney interrupted me." But she couldn't say that because then he would demand to know why she'd been crying. She was too emotionally drained to even attempt to explain to him how she'd felt when she'd seen him holding Phyllis. Just the memory of it hurt. How could she possibly talk about it—to him. She didn't want to hear some glib lie that would supposedly explain everything, a lie she would desperately want to believe.

"Tell me!"

"He was removing an eyelash because my eye was watering," she hedged.

His eyes were on her face, and he was staring at her intently. She felt increasingly uncomfortable. His gaze was penetrating; he saw too much. She hadn't told him the whole truth, and she was sure that fact was guiltily written on her face. When she tried to look away he sprang from his desk and cupped her face in his large brown hands. He stared at her for a long moment. At last he released her.

His eyes were the deepest, darkest shade of blue. "You've never been any good at lying, Kit," he said. "You've been acting very strangely all day. I'm wondering if you're regretting our marriage. Did you call him when I left at noon? Are you planning to see him again? Kit, are you sorry you broke your engagement to him—and married me?"

He was still staring at her closely through narrowed

eyes, as though he thought the answers to his questions would be inscribed on her face. She flushed guiltily and squirmed.

He had no right to question her like this. She should be questioning him. After all he was the one who was actually involved with someone else.

She remembered him holding Phyllis tightly in his arms with the waves swirling around them. They were in love; it was obvious. There could be no other explanation. If he was in love with his sister-in-law, why did he care what she, Kit, did in any case?

He didn't; he couldn't really care, she decided bitterly. He was just proud. He didn't want it known his wife might be the unfaithful type. It wouldn't reflect well on his masculine image.

"Kit, what does Rodney mean to you?"

"He means nothing to me! And I don't like being accused of things when I'm not guilty! Why won't you believe me?"

"Perhaps it has something to do with your walking out on me five years ago without telling me why. It's a little hard for me to trust you when I remember that." He grasped her wrist. "Tell me, Kit, what is going on?"

He seemed determined to believe her guilty. He did not trust her! If only she had the proper sense of humor she could have laughed, the situation was so absurd. But she was too deeply hurt.

He was implying that she wanted to have an affair with Rodney when all the time he was probably actually having one with Phyllis. The irony of it tasted bitter in her mouth, and she swallowed convulsively.

He had no right to accuse her unjustly! And she had no desire to accuse him although he was guilty! The situation was hopeless.

"Would you please let go of me," she said at last.

"You're hurting me." When he released her, her wrist was red from his touch.

"Tell me, Kit, what's going on!"

She looked up from rubbing her injured wrist, straight into his eyes. "I've told you the truth, and I have nothing more to say," she replied flatly. "But it's clear what kind of woman you think I am. I don't suppose that should surprise me—considering the kind of man you are. Living the way you do, it's no wonder you think I'm capable of being married to one man and sneaking around to see another. But, you can relax, I'm not cheating on you. And I won't—ever. I am not that kind of person. Your masculine pride is intact—I'm sure that's all that matters to you—really—in any case."

"Damn it, Kit. I couldn't care less about my 'masculine pride' as you put it. All I've ever cared about is . . ." He seemed to think better of what he'd intended to say and paused. Kit wondered if he'd almost said the name "Phyllis." He continued, "And I want to know what you mean by such remarks as 'considering the kind of man I am.' I'm getting a little sick of your insinuations. Insinuations you refuse to explain. Perhaps now is a good time to bring up the past. I'd like to know why you left me when we were in college."

"You were the one who once said our discussions about the past always dead-end. And I see no reason to explain the obvious. Now if you'll excuse me, I think I'll take the rest of the afternoon off. I don't think I could accomplish anything further; the atmosphere isn't conducive to work. Anyway, I'm sure you haven't forgotten for one minute that you invited Phyllis over. I need to go to the grocery store and straighten the house."

He didn't so much as twitch an eyebrow at the mention of Phyllis's name. Grudgingly Kit had an odd sense of admiration for his superb ability to conceal his true emotions.

She stood up, and for a minute, she didn't think he was going to allow her to leave. He was staring down at her so hard, she thought he could see right through her.

"All right," he managed more calmly. "We don't seem to be getting anywhere with this discussion." He thrust his hand into his pocket and produced his key. "Take my car. If I need to go somewhere, I'll take one of the vans."

Kit spent the afternoon getting ready for their dinner guests. She'd never felt less in the mood for a dinner party. The bitter words lingered in her mind, and she felt acutely unhappy.

She'd been a silly, romantic fool to have married him. She'd irrationally thought that her love for him would be enough to solve all their problems. But she hadn't anticipated his involvement with another woman. He probably thought it his right to be married to one woman and in love with another. . . .

Ted returned home in time to start the fire for the steaks. Kit had already put potatoes into the oven to bake and tossed a salad. She'd gone to a bookstore and bought herself two cookbooks. She'd also gone to a bakery and selected a chocolate cake for Missy.

When Ted came in from the balcony where he'd been tending the fire, he did not offer to apologize for the unpleasant scene that had passed between them. His blue gaze raked coldly over her, taking in every detail of her appearance. She was wearing her green sundress again—he'd told her several times he thought she looked especially beautiful in it. She'd piled her hair high on top of her head in a new hairstyle she'd seen in a magazine. But if he found her attractive, he did not say so.

Instead he went to the bar and mixed himself a drink. She observed his mouth set in a thin, forbidding line; the angular planes of his face were harsh. She couldn't help noticing he'd mixed himself a double. Was her company so unendurable for him that he needed a stiff drink to stand being near her?

Her eyes smarted with tears. How was she going to make it through this evening—entertaining Phyllis?

Ted was showering when the doorbell rang, so Kit had to answer it. She pasted what she hoped was a warm smile on her face and opened the door. She didn't want to give Phyllis the satisfaction of seeing how unhappy she really was.

Missy bounded into the house.

"Kit, where's Joseph?" Her bright, blue eyes danced.

"You know he's upstairs just waiting for you to come visit him."

The child dashed up the carpeted stairs.

"Come on in, Phyllis," Kit said in the cheeriest voice she could muster.

Phyllis eyed her with a frosty, gray stare and a quick twist of her lips and stepped inside.

Ted came out of the bedroom. His auburn hair glistened with wetness. He was wearing a pale blue shirt that was open at the throat. Kit watched the hard contours of his muscled leanness ripple beneath the cotton fabric of his shirt as he moved toward Phyllis. He was wearing corduroy jeans of a darker shade of blue that were belted around his narrow waist. Kit caught the fragrance of his after shave, the fresh laundry-smell of his shirt.

"Hello, Phyllis. I'm glad you could come. You look beautiful." His drawl was painfully resonant with warmth and friendliness.

Kit was reminded he'd scarcely spoken to her since their argument at the store. Nor had he complimented her appearance even though she'd worked very hard to look nice for him. Unhappily Kit watched him bend over Phyllis and kiss her lightly on the cheek as he helped her out of her jacket.

"I'm . . . I'm glad I could come too," Phyllis answered in choked tones.

"Princess." Ted's voice was vibrant with emotion. Missy was descending the stairs dragging her battered rabbit friend and carrying several story books. "Let me help you with all that." He lifted her and her things into his arms. "What's my little princess been up to?" He set the child down and bent to her level, and she told him about the pet gerbil Amie Rodgers had brought to kindergarten class that morning.

Throughout dinner conversation was stilted, and Ted did most of the talking in an effort to cover up the awkward silences. He was very friendly to Phyllis and tried hard but without much success to see that she enjoyed her evening.

Phyllis scarcely ate a bite of food. She spoke only when asked a direct question. It wasn't difficult for Kit to understand how she felt, for she herself felt the same way.

To Kit, Ted was civil, but his manner lacked warmth. Kit was sure that Phyllis sensed there was something wrong between them. After dessert Missy decided it was story time.

"I want Aunt Phyllis to sit here and Daddy here," she said, plopping down on the couch and indicating either side of her small self. Kit realized the child wasn't intentionally leaving her out. Missy just wasn't accustomed to her yet and didn't know how she fit into her life.

Kit was clearing the dishes from the table as Phyllis and Ted joined the child on the couch.

"Would you like to read 'Cinderella?'" Phyllis asked innocently.

"Isn't that the one about the wicked stepmother?" the child queried.

"Yes, dear, it is," Phyllis said in carefully measured tones, looking up from the brightly-colored story book and staring with direct coldness across the room at Kit.

Either unaware of or determined to ignore the undercurrents in the room, Ted began, "Once upon a time there lived . . ."

Watching them read together—their dark heads bent over the book—Kit thought they looked like the ideal family. Each adult took turns answering Missy's eager questions. It was obvious this was a ritual they all enjoyed that had gone on ever since Letitia's death. The resonant cadence of Ted's voice filled the room, and Kit had never felt more left out in her life than she did listening to the three of them reading and discussing "Cinderella."

Later Missy decided she wanted her daddy to take her down to the water and search for crabs. When they left, Phyllis offered to help Kit with the dishes, and Kit could think of no way to refuse her.

After a strained silence, Kit attempted small talk.

"You look awfully nice tonight in that dress, Phyllis. In fact, this may surprise you, but I almost bought one like it the other day myself when I was shopping."

"Really, why didn't you?"

"Well, I just didn't have the time to try it on what with the wedding preparations and all."

Phyllis almost dropped the plate she was drying at the mention of the word "wedding," but she managed to catch it before it hit the porcelain sink. She pressed her lips tightly together and made no comment as she dried the plate furiously.

"I love the office you decorated for me, Phyllis. I thought the wallpaper was lovely."

"You just won't stop, will you? I decorated it for Ted—not you!" Phyllis said cruelly. "I'm sure you must've realized that! And furthermore, you needn't try to entertain me with your mindless chatter. Nothing you have to say could be of the slightest interest to me." She set the plate down on the counter with a clatter. "I know that sounds rude, but I just can't be a hypocrite like you. I know you don't like me any more than I like you."

Kit gasped.

"Not that you should. As I've said I don't like you either. And I don't like what you're doing to Ted and Missy. It's obvious to me that Ted is very unhappy. He hardly said a word to you tonight, and that's not like him. You've only been married a few days, but I guess he's finding out what kind of woman you are."

"Phyllis," Kit interrupted in a quiet voice, "you are in my home as a guest, and you have no right to say these things to me. If you can't be pleasant, you'll have to leave. I'm not up . . ."

"You always expect to get your way, don't you?" Phyllis challenged. "Well, this is the real world and you're all grown up. Your wealthy father can't give it all to you anymore. It's time you learned just wanting a man and trapping him into marriage aren't enough to keep him."

The front door opened and slammed shut before Kit

had a chance to retaliate. Missy bounded into the room chattering about all the sea creatures they'd seen and the fisherman she'd talked to.

Kit sighed with relief, and Phyllis lapsed into a long and stony silence until Ted escorted Missy and her home.

As soon as they were out the door, Kit went into the bedroom. Phyllis must have felt very sure of herself as far as Ted was concerned or she would never have said those things she'd said in the kitchen. Dismally, Kit changed into a filmy nightnown the color of flame. She put on a matching see-through peignoir. Phyllis's words seemed to repeat themselves in her brain as she uncoiled the length of her long black hair and let it fall like a thick veil to her shoulders. She brushed her hair free of all tangles and then went to the bed.

She knew she couldn't sleep—she was too distraught. She selected a mystery novel Ted had read and recommended and slipped into bed with it. Although the novel was written by an author whose tight prose and fast-moving tales usually kept her reading spellbound from the first sentence to the last, she couldn't get past the first paragraph. She read it over four times before she closed the book and set it in her lap.

What was wrong with her? Why couldn't she just accept the fact that Phyllis and Ted were in love and step aside so they could be happy together? But the thought of losing Ted completely was devastating. She'd been through that once before. She had a stubborn streak as well, and she loved him so much she kept clinging to the flimsy hope that things could work out.

She placed the book on the bedside table. She might as well turn out the light. She couldn't read anyway.

After what seemed an eternity of lying sleepless in the dark, she heard the sound of Ted's footsteps outside and of the front door opening and closing. She heard his tread—heavy upon the plush carpet as he headed toward their bedroom.

He opened the bedroom door slowly and switched on the light. She kept her eyes squeezed tightly shut and pretended she was asleep.

"I doubt very much you're asleep," he said perceptively. "I want to talk to you." He crossed the room with long rapid strides and sat on the corner of the bed at her feet.

"Well, I don't want to talk to you," she said, sitting up and brushing her mussed hair back from her face. Something about the authoritative tone in his voice upset her. She blinked her eyes against the brightness of the now-lighted room.

"Don't you think it's a mistake to go to bed with this argument between us," he said in softer tones, his blue eyes somber.

"Yes, I do, but as I didn't start the argument, I don't believe it's up to me to clear the air. I seem to remember it was you who falsely accused me of chasing after Rodney. However, if you're ready to apologize, I'll listen."

"I have no intention of apologizing about anything," he said grimly. "You still haven't told me what you were doing in his arms."

His steady blue eyes never left her face. His face was white and drawn—like that of a man bleeding from an internal wound. Still, he was handsome, the handsomest man she'd ever seen. But his arrogant assumption of her guilt enabled her to steel herself against his appeal.

"Ted," she begged abruptly, wishing there could be

peace between them once more although she was unwilling to relent from her own position, "you must believe that what I told you earlier was the truth. You must!"

"Without any further explanation?"

"Yes."

"You ask too much," he said at last in a quiet, toneless voice.

Her heart sank with bitter disappointment. He refused to believe in her; he refused to trust her.

Anger flared in her suddenly. He'd been with Phyllis for over an hour, and he had the nerve to resume this ridiculous argument with her!

"You have your nerve!" she began, her black eyes flashing. "You think you can do exactly what you please and it shouldn't make any difference at all to me. You've been with Phyllis for over an hour, and have I said one thing? No!"

His hard gaze flicked over her. When he spoke his voice was tight with control. "My relationship with Phyllis is not at all the same thing. I was over there putting Missy to bed—you know that."

"No, I don't!"

"Phyllis is my sister-in-law! I have to see her from time to time because of Missy. She also happens to be a very good friend of mine. You're just throwing this out as a red herring."

"Am I? It's all right for you but not for me. Is that it?"

"You were in Rodney's arms," he accused. "I saw you myself."

"And you were holding Phyllis in your arms on our wedding night," she wanted to lash out. But she didn't. As always her belief that he would lie glibly and she would foolishly long to believe him stopped her. Aloud she said, "I told you all he did was remove an eyelash from my eye."

Wearily he rose from the bed. He began pulling out blankets and sheets.

"What are you going to do?" she asked shakily.

"I'm going to sleep on the couch, if it's of any real interest to you," he replied steadily.

Then he left her, and she felt numbed with the pain of his rejection and lack of faith in her.

Was this to be their marriage? Coldness and distrust? It was almost morning before Kit fell into a troubled sleep.

Chapter Nine

The sun—hot and angry—like a great ball of flame hovered on the horizon where water touched sky. Pink light was filtering though the bedroom draperies when Kit stumbled out of bed.

Ted was knocking briskly on the door.

"Come in," she called, pulling her filmy peignoir hastily over her shoulders.

"Thought I heard you up," he said.

His dark skin was shadowy beneath his eyes; he hadn't slept any better than she. His long frame probably hadn't fit the couch too comfortably.

He was shirtless, wearing only the bottoms of his blue pajamas. A towel slung carelessly over one shoulder was white against the mat of dark hair covering the breadth of his bronzed chest. Weakly she observed the contours of his muscles, his hard leanness.

She wished there was some way she could make him believe her.

But, more than that she wished there was some way she could make him love her.

Without another word to her, he went to his closet and began rummaging through his clothes, taking some out and throwing them on the bed. The pile began to mount.

"What are you doing?" she asked tonelessly.

"I think you can see that for yourself. I'm moving some of my things upstairs."

Her voice almost caught in her throat, but she managed, "Why?"

"I would think you'd be grateful instead of so inquisitive," he answered, his voice hard, his blue eyes cold. "I seem to remember that you wanted me to marry you on one condition: that I not touch you. Well, I promise you, I have no intention of touching you again. Not that you would care. Lately you've made it very clear you want to have as little to do with me as possible." He grabbed a handful of hangers on which hung his suits, slacks, and dress shirts. When one of the shirts slipped from the hanger, she rushed to retrieve it. "I can manage without your help," he said curtly.

Stung, she made no further attempt to assist him.

"You're still furious about Rodney's visit to the store, aren't you?" When he made no reply, she said, "Why won't you believe me when I say nothing happened?"

"I've told you. You're a terrible liar, and you lied about Rodney. Or at least if you didn't actually lie . . . you're holding something back. And I keep wondering what it is and why."

"There's nothing between Rodney and me."

"There had better not be! I'm not the kind of man who wants to share his wife with any man."

"There isn't another man."

He made no reply.

"Does this mean you want a divorce?" she asked hesitantly.

He threw the hangers onto the bed. He came toward her and seized her by the wrist, pulling her up hard against him. The peignoir fell from her shoulders revealing clearly to him her lovely curves in the filmy nightgown. His gaze drifted slowly over her body, and she blushed hotly. The knowing look in his eyes made her acutely conscious of his blatant virility.

"No! It doesn't!" he rasped in a strangely hoarse voice. "And don't mention that word to me again."

He released her hand, and resumed his task of removing his clothes.

So—he was still furious because she hadn't explained Rodney's visit to his satisfaction.

She almost screamed that she was the one who should be angry—not him. That he was blaming her for what he himself was guilty of. That it was his own guilty conscience tormenting him.

During the succeeding weeks she saw little of him. He threw himself into his work with a vengeance and began to work late into the evenings. She knew that he was doing it deliberately so he could avoid her. When she was at his store, he found excuses to be at some construction site. When she was at home, he said he had to work after hours at the store to catch up on paper work. Evenings when he didn't work, he either went over to Phyllis's and visited with Missy or down to the yacht club to work on *Wild Lady*.

Their marriage consisted of coldly polite salutations passing between them in the mornings and evenings.

Kit was desperately unhappy. She'd lost weight. If she hadn't had her work at the store to occupy herself with, she would have gone mad.

She loved him—still, but their marriage seemed hopeless.

It was the evening of the Starr ball, the night before the Starr cattle auction. Ted had spent two days at the Starr Ranch personally supervising his men setting up the tents, and dancefloors, tables and chairs.

When he came home early that evening, he looked exhausted.

She was already dressed for the ball in a gown that was simple in design and stunning. The dress was wine red; the deep color enhanced her own dark coloring. The soft material rounded beneath her breasts and fell to the floor.

She was brushing her black hair when he came into the bedroom. His skin was tanned mahogany brown from the long days spent in the sun; his wind-blown hair glinted gold. He sagged wearily against the door frame, his gaze traveling slowly over her. Tired as he looked, just for an instant she saw a faint leaping light in his eyes. He wanted her. She knew it. But he didn't want her to know. Abruptly he looked away.

A wave of tenderness rushed through her at the sight of him looking so haggard. "Ted, you really do look awfully tired," she said gently. "Maybe we should stay home and have a quiet evening together."

His eyes went over her again and his expression darkened. "I am tired, but I would prefer to go to the party," he said tonelessly. "I need to go . . . for business reasons. I'll just take a quick shower and change."

He left her and trudged heavily upstairs. When he was gone she wanted to collapse onto the bed in tears. He hated her. She knew he did. He preferred going to the party when he was exhausted to spending an evening home alone with her. He had said nothing about her new dress and how lovely she looked in it. Although it was a small thing, this omission hurt. She'd tried so hard to be beautiful for him, hoping his attitude toward her might soften.

She'd seen desire in his eyes, but he'd fought against it. He disliked her so much he didn't even want to find her attractive.

They rode in silence to the Starr Ranch. He made no attempt to talk to her. Occasionally she would catch a glimpse of his features as the headlights of a car passed them. His face was full of menace—he looked almost dangerous. It seemed to her that her mere presence provoked him in some way she could not understand.

As they turned from the highway onto the curving asphalt drive that led to the ranch house, the moon—golden and full—was just rising. They were directed by a ranch hand to a canopied walkway that led to the enormous sprawling mansion.

The party had a flavor that was distinctly Texan. If only things had been right with her marriage, Kit would have enjoyed herself. The scent of hickory and barbecue wafted in the crisp, cool night air. Kit heard the whine of western music. She saw that although some of the guests that strolled arm-in-arm across the lawns wore formal gowns and jewels, others wore boots and cowboy hats.

Matt Walsh, Rodney's older cousin and one of the owners of the vast ranching empire, was one of the hosts. He came to greet them. Her own brother Steve with Alicia Walsh, Matt's younger sister, on his arm was right behind Matt. Alicia, golden and lovely in the moonlight, wore a gown of yellow froth.

"You did a great job with the tents, Bradley," Matt was saying.

Movies flickered across one large screen in a nearby tent to acquaint guests with the cattle and horses that would be auctioned on the following day. Hors d'oeuvres were being served beneath another tent.

"And, Kit," Matt continued in a fatherly way, "you look gorgeous. I think marriage suits you." He took her hand in his and led her beneath the canopies across the grounds. He offered her and her husband hors d'oeuvres. Shrimp teriyaki and petite finger ribs were being grilled over open flames.

Matt was trying to be hospitable. In spite of Matt's friendliness, Ted's mood darkened with each hospitable comment the other man made.

Matt was complimenting Kit. "Bradley, I'm sure you're aware that your wife epitomizes the beauty of South Texas. She represents how beautifully two cultures—the Spanish and the American—can blend. Tonight she looks like a Spanish princess."

The lines beside Ted's mouth tightened as Kit blushed, laughing nervously, and thanked Matt for his compliment, but Ted said nothing. He merely drained his drink and reached for another. Kit could see that it was going to be a long evening.

The sound of Spanish music drifted from the porch where *mariachis* were singing and playing their guitars. Kit absently tapped her foot in time with the music.

Matt was telling them of the notable guests. "The governor, of course, always comes, and tonight an Arab prince is here. I'll introduce you to Namir after a while. An African prime minister . . . cattle buyers from South America . . ."

Conversation turned to cattle; and Steve, Matt, and Ted began discussing the auction. Kit knew Ted was interested in buying some stock for his ranch in The Valley.

A small dark man in flowing white robes approached. He seized Kit by the hand and introduced himself as Prince Namir. His English was impeccable. He seemed filled with energy. His black eyes flashed and his hands moved nervously as he talked. He paid her outrageous compliments, and she found herself laughing at their absurdity. He told her she had harem eyes, that she was like a desert flower. When he asked her to dance, she accepted.

As Prince Namir danced with her she glanced occasionally in Ted's direction. He was still conversing with her brother.

Prince Namir danced with her once, twice, and then a third time. His energy was boundless. The music stopped and he asked her for a fourth dance. She was about to refuse him, but as she glanced again toward Ted, she saw that he was now talking to a beautiful, elegantly-clad woman.

"Why not?" Kit responded pertly to the dark Arab, and he hugged her to him.

The dance was a fast one, and when it ended she was laughing breathlessly. Prince Namir led her from the dance floor. Ted was still talking to the beautiful woman.

When Prince Namir offered her a glass of champagne, she hesitated. She hadn't eaten, and champagne on an empty stomach . . . Then she giggled, "Why not?" She felt hollow, as though she were filled with a strange coldness. Perhaps a glass . . . or two would warm her and make her forget . . .

She sipped her champagne and noticed the beautiful woman laughing at something Ted had said to her. Then she saw him laugh. Achingly Kit thought that it had been so long, too long . . . since he'd laughed with her.

Ted was dancing with the woman now, and he was holding her close. Then Kit watched them no longer, for Prince Namir was back and demanding her attention for himself.

When dinner was served, Prince Namir was again at her side. The dinner menu featured chicken curry with condiments: chutney and raisins, over wild rice, chilled tenderloin; baked acorn squash filled with fresh pineapple. The salad consisted of whole marinated artichokes, mushrooms and crisp lettuce leaves.

Kit couldn't eat a bite. She had no appetite. She did however watch Namir gobble every morsel from his plate. When dessert was served he selected tart lemon bars and fruit-glazed brie. They in turn quickly vanished from his plate.

When he finished his meal, Namir again gave Kit his full attention. Again he paid her absurd compliments, saying he pitied the sultans of old because she had not been one of their harem girls.

"And have you a harem, Prince Namir?" she asked. What was the harm of flirting with him? It had been so long since her own husband had made her feel attractive.

He laughed as if he found that idea delightful. "Er . . . not exactly. I have one wife . . . and . . . er . . . occasionally . . . I meet other women who delight me as you do. Our customs are different from yours.

154

We make allowances for the nature of men. You Americans set too much store upon fidelity."

She thought of Ted and found Prince Namir's remarks ironic. "And your wife . . . she thinks as you do?"

"What she thinks does not matter. She is only a woman. We have our customs."

"Sometimes I think they're not so different from our own."

"I do not like to talk about my wife when I'm with a woman as beautiful as you," Prince Namir said.

"Don't you? How exceedingly thoughtful." She giggled merrily up at him as she sipped her champagne.

After dinner he asked her to dance. The music was slow, and he held her close, pressing her to him. She looked over his shoulder once and was aware of Ted watching her from the shadows. He looked lean and darkly elegant, but his expression was so harsh, she could have wept. But she was at a party and she was determined to have fun. When the dance ended Prince Namir handed her another glass of champagne. She drank it hoping it would blot out the dark vision of Ted's countenance.

Other men asked her to dance: Steve, her father, Matt, and men she'd met only for the first time at the party. Once the governor himself claimed a dance. As she whirled in their arms she was unaware of how devastatingly beautiful she was with her wine-red gown swirling around her lithe figure, her black hair shimmering in the moonlight. She laughed too frequently, but if her laughter sounded strangely brittle as it blended with the music, no one seemed to notice. She appeared the picture of gaiety even though her heart was breaking.

She found herself suddenly alone. She was reaching for a third glass of champagne, when a large brown hand clamped around her wrist.

"I think you've had enough for one evening," Ted said.

The moon washed all color from his face. Only his eyes were alive. They flashed brilliant like the blue fire of a gas jet.

For some reason she was afraid of him. "I was just having fun," she said defiantly.

Matt, Howard and Steve were approaching and to avoid talking to them, Ted said, "I want you to dance with me. I have something to say to you."

"Well, I don't have anything to say to you!"

Just as the three men joined them, she twisted free of Ted's grasp. "If you'll all excuse me . . ." She tried to make her shaking voice sound light. "I promised Prince Namir this dance." Then she raced off into the night.

She danced again and again and again. She wanted to dance until she was too exhausted to think or feel anything about Ted. Several hours passed before she realized that she had not once caught sight of him since he'd asked her to dance. Where was he? She glanced at her diamond wrist watch. It was nearly three A.M.

When most of the guests had gone, Kit began searching for Ted. She ran across the grounds until she was breathless. Where had he gone? A branch of a twisting live oak snagged her gown and tore it, but she was so distracted she scarcely noticed.

Matt came to her. His pale hair gleamed like a silver halo in the moonlight.

"Something wrong, Kit?"

"I was looking for Ted."

"I think I saw him leaving with your brother and his date around midnight."

"Leaving . . . without . . ." Her voice faltered.

Matt eyed her sympathetically. "You two having problems?" Her eyes were over-large and glazed with pain. There was no sign of the gay creature who'd whirled madly in the wine-red gown. She nodded mutely. "Let's go see if your car's still here," he said gently. "If it is I'll drive you home."

The car was parked exactly where they'd left it earlier. The keys were in the ignition, and a terse note was clipped to the visor, which read,

"Kit,
Tried to tell you I was tired and ready to go.
Caught a ride with your brother. Ted."

Matt was opening the door for her. He slipped behind the wheel.

"Matt, you don't have to drive . . ."

"You're in no condition to drive, Kit," he said in a determined voice.

They drove home in silence, the only sounds that of the big engine's purr and that of Kit crumpling and uncrumpling the stiff paper Ted had scribbled his note on.

When they arrived at her townhouse, it was unlighted.

"I'll come inside just for a minute to make sure everything's all right," Matt said.

Together they went inside. Kit switched on the lights and went from room to room, her voice echoing as she called to Ted. There was no sign that he'd even been there.

"Matt, where could he be? It's nearly four A.M.?" she asked worriedly.

157

"You said the two of you have been having problems. He could . . ."

His remark set her thinking along a different track. Phyllis! He could be over there.

How she summoned the courage to dial Phyllis's number she never knew. But she had to know if her worst fears were true. She couldn't go on doubting him. When Phyllis answered in a fuzzy voice, Kit blurted, "Phyllis, this is Kit. I'm terribly worried about Ted. He hasn't come home from the Starr ball and I was wondering if you know where he might be."

"He's here. Asleep." Phyllis replied icily, before hanging up on her.

He was asleep at Phyllis's! Her worst suspicions were true! Something seemed to shatter inside her.

"Kit, is he . . ." Matt's hand covered hers that was holding the buzzing receiver. He hung up the phone.

"He's with Phyllis," she replied dully.

"I doubt if it's the way it seems. Ted wouldn't . . ."

"It's exactly the way it seems. He did the same thing before . . ." she wailed desperately.

She was in his arms without knowing quite how she got there and he was pressing her head against his shoulder.

Keys were rattling in the lock of the front door, and Ted stepped inside. He looked completely exhausted. His eyes were red, the dark flesh beneath them puffy and shadowed. His elegant navy suit was badly wrinkled. His hair was disheveled and tumbling over his brow. Every inch of him seem to sag with weariness, and for a split second Kit's heart went out to him. Then she remembered he'd spent the night with Phyllis.

When Ted saw her in Matt's arms, his face hardened, his eyes glittered with emotion.

"Darn you, Kit!" he muttered at last. Then more to

himself than to her: "I don't know why I'm blaming you. I should have known the kind of woman you were when I married you." He was advancing upon her. "You don't know me very well if you think I'll put up with a wife who chases every man she sees and then brings one home for the night." He gripped her by the hand, pulling her away from Matt. "I want you out of here! Now! Take your things and get out!" He picked up her evening bag and wrap she'd set on a chair and pushed them into her fingers. "Come back for the rest of your things during the day—when I'm at work—so I won't have to see you again!"

"Ted, I can explain. It's not what you think."

"I said get out! Both of you!" An odd smile twisted his lips. He released Kit's hand, and moved toward Matt. Never had he looked so ruthless . . . so menacing.

Matt stiffened. "Bradley, you're jumping to the wrong conclusion."

"Walsh, if you're smart, you'll get out like I asked—before I lose control . . ."

"Ted . . ." Kit began weakly, desperately.

"Get out, Kit! I don't want to see you—ever again!"

Chapter Ten

A splash of sunflowers was bright gaiety against the stark flat stretch of cactus and brown grass that was the Starr Ranch. The Jackson Lincoln and its occupants sped beneath the ebony trees that lined either side of the asphalt road that wound past the big ranch house and the adobe brick horse stables to the shaded arena where the cattle auction would be held.

"I really wish you'd let me stay home," Kit said to the group in general.

"You need to be out with people—not at home moping," her father declared.

"The auction will take your mind off your troubles," Anitra amended gently. "Perhaps this will be the very thing to help you put this . . . this lovers' quarrel into the proper perspective."

Matt had caught a ride with them because he'd driven Kit home the night before and left his own car at the ranch. "If you want me to talk to Bradley, Kit, I will," he offered. "There's no reason for the two of you to separate because of a misunderstanding over me."

"No! I've told you there's much more to it than that! And there's no reason for all of you to concern yourselves with my problems. I'll handle them my own way."

"You're not doing such a terrific job of it at the moment, Sis," Steve said. "You may be as mistaken about what he was doing at Phyllis's as he is about Matt. The two of you need to sit down and have a long talk."

Though Kit could appreciate the logic of Steve's statement, she knew that such a "talk" would never be possible. She'd seen the look of implacable hatred on Ted's face when he'd thrown her out last night.

He was probably deeply relieved to have her out of his life for good. Whatever attraction he had for her, whatever whim had prompted him to marry her no longer existed. She was simply in the way. He wanted Phyllis not her. Why couldn't he have realized that long ago? Before they'd married? Before they'd gotten involved with one another all over again? She knew that losing him this time would hurt far worse than losing him the first time.

Now she was a woman. She'd experienced the deepest sexual and spiritual fulfillment in his arms. She knew that no man would claim her heart again in the same deeply complete way he had.

Anitra, her daughter's problems forgotten for the moment, was chattering gaily, but Kit wasn't listening. She felt dead, as though she was only going through the motions of being alive. Would it always be like this—without him? She remembered the five long empty years before he'd come back into her life.

Kit saw the future, the years of her life stretching before her, and without Ted, they seemed a lifetime of desolation. She sat quietly, her hands folded in her lap, her whole body taut, as she struggled for composure. Her lips pressed themselves into a tight line. She made no attempt to brush away the single tear that spilled over her eyelashes and traced a glistening path down her cheek. She was not even aware that it had fallen.

The Jacksons drove past open cattle trucks parked along the side of the road. After they passed a cluster of shorter horse trailers nestled beneath the shade of a few feathery salt cedar, Howard maneuvered the car off the road and onto a field that was being used as a parking lot and parked the car. They got out of the car and headed for the arena.

Spanish music was a slur of sound; the scent of cattle and horses was in the air. Barbecue was being served beneath the shade of several large party tents. Kit saw, perched on high stools at one of the many tables covered with red-checkered table cloths and not too far from the band, Ted, Phyllis and Missy. They were eating barbecue.

Ted looked even more haggard than he had the night before. He was wearing a red and green plaid western shirt, faded jeans and boots. His cowboy hat was pushed back from his face, and she saw that his auburn hair was uncombed, that a lock of it kept falling across his dark brow. His face was darkly shadowed as if he hadn't shaved. He looked up and saw her just as a voice on the loud speaker announced that the auction would begin in ten minutes, and Steve placed a hand beneath her elbow to lead her to the arena. As soon as he saw her, Ted turned quickly away as if the very sight of her caused him pain.

He was free of her. Didn't he realize she was willing

for him to live his life as he wished? She would place no further claim on him. She wondered if he felt guilty to be with another woman when he was still legally married to her.

The shade of the covered arena was welcome after the brilliance of the Texas sun. Spanish guitars whined in the background as some of the ranch workers watered down the saw dust in the auction block that resembled a cattle pen. Only the faintest breeze stirred the air.

Kit watched as Ted, his hand cupping Phyllis's elbow, found a seat not too far from her. Not once did he turn to look at her.

The guitar music faded, and the rumbling voice of the auctioneer began. The crowd murmured as a small, fat cowboy led two thousand pounds of excitement, a Santa Gertrudis bull, into the arena. The small cowboy handled the powerful bull with expert ease as if the animal were no more than a small dog he was leading on a leash.

With the careless disregard of children playing with play money, wealthy ranchers began bidding and the bull's price quickly soared to five figures.

Three bulls later Kit watched Ted's hand go up. He was bidding on one of the finer bulls Matt had mentioned the night before. The bidding went hot and fast, and when it was over Ted had purchased a very fine piece of livestock. He bid on two more bulls with impeccable bloodlines and bought them. After he bid on the third bull he got up and ushered Phyllis and Missy out of the arena. Never once did he glance in Kit's direction, and she knew that he was avoiding her deliberately.

Kit's heart was an aching place in her breast. She could barely sit through the auction. Oh, why had she let her parents bring her? She should have stayed home. It was terrible seeing Ted with Phyllis. He, on the other hand, obviously felt perfectly all right or he couldn't have come and bid on three bulls as if nothing of any consequence had happened to him.

It was a relief a few minutes later when Howard came to her and said her family was ready to leave.

The big Lincoln sped back toward town. Anitra chattered gaily. Kit stared silently and unseeingly out the window.

Farmland like black felt pierced with oil dereks stretched on all sides of the speeding car. The terrain was stark and vast and empty, the sky a brilliant sweep of blue, blurring at the horizon because of the heat waves.

Kit brushed at the tears falling lightly down her cheeks. She felt her heart was like the view outside—a vast, aching emptiness.

A week passed—the longest week of Kit's life. She still hadn't felt up to returning to Ted's townhouse for her things.

It was eight o'clock in the morning. Saturday. The start for the first race of the new yacht series would be at ten. Kit's father had insisted she come down to breakfast.

She was buttering her toast when Howard announced, "Kit, I need you to crew today. Jake just called and he can't make it."

"Daddy, surely you haven't forgotten the disaster . . ."

"No, I haven't. But I need you, and you need to get out of the house. It isn't good for you to spend so much time alone in your room. Besides you don't have a thing to worry about. I won't let you near the tiller."

"Is Ted . . ."

"Yes, he'll be racing. *Wild Lady*'s back in the water. I helped him tune the mast the other evening."

"Then I definitely won't go."

"Yes, you will. It's time you thought of someone besides yourself for a change. I need you."

When he put it like that, she couldn't refuse him. They were at the pier rigging *Kitten,* when Kit looked up and saw the ice blue hull of *Wild Lady* slicing through the waves. He and Phyllis were sitting very close to one another in the stern of the boat, and the sight of them together was a vicious pain in her heart.

Ted saw her then, and for one long minute his eyes fastened on her as he drank in every detail of her appearance. Then he tacked abruptly, and *Wild Lady* headed off in another direction.

Had he noticed how much weight she'd lost in the past seven days? Had he seen the bluish half-moons beneath her eyes—evidence that her nights were long and sleepless? And if he saw, would he care that she was desperately unhappy? After all, *he had Phyllis.*

Wild Lady was the last boat across the starting line.

"Looks like we won't have any worries where Bradley's concerned," her father commented. "He's definitely chosen the wrong tack."

Kit, who was hanging onto *Kitten* for dear life, observed *Wild Lady* tacking away from the fleet toward the shore.

"He won't improve his position doing that," her father continued. "His judgment's way off."

At the windward mark Ted was even further behind than he'd been at the start. Kit couldn't imagine what was wrong. Her father said that he'd been on *Wild Lady* Wednesday night and the boat had sailed perfectly.

Howard Jackson finished way ahead of all the other boats; Ted finished way behind them.

After the race, Howard told his daughter and son that he wanted to have a drink in the club before returning home.

The white-coated waiter was taking their orders. "What will you have, Mrs. Bradley?" Skip asked her. His pencil hovered over his notepad as he waited for her to make up her mind.

"I guess I'll have a Coke . . . with a touch of lime in it," she responded indifferently. His pencil was scribbling on paper when Ted and Phyllis walked into the bar. Kit looked up and saw them. "No, Skip, let me change that she amended hastily, "to a . . . a martini. And make it a stiff one."

She observed Ted's appearance achingly. In spite of his haggard expression he looked terribly handsome. His auburn hair was tousled from the wind. His white shirt—its top three buttons undone—was startling white against the darkness of his massive, darkly-tanned chest. He wore dungarees—neatly belted around his narrow waist. She saw the rippling contours of his muscles, his taut leanness.

She noted that the lines about his eyes were unusually deep—that he looked tired. She saw that his lips were parted in a half-smile over something Phyllis was saying.

Never had having drinks with friends been such an ordeal. How she'd ever gotten through it, she never knew.

Her father was basking in glory. He was the undisputed victor. Everyone surrounded him and congratulated him. They were asking why he'd selected his smaller spinnaker rather than his heavy-air spinnaker.

"Just by feel," he answered proudly. "I felt like the light-air spinnaker would do the job."

"I sure miscalculated on that one," Marc Clay said. "Did you see the knock-down we took?"

"Well, you needn't feel too ashamed, you placed second," Kris said. "Bradley over there seems to have miscalculated on everything." There was no malice in his voice. He was just teasing good-naturedly. "Sorry about that, Bradley," he added in louder tones. "but you've gotta expect a few remarks when you bomb out. You usually do so well. It's not often we get the chance to rib you."

Bradley looked up from his drink and smiled at Kris, but he made no comment. His blue gaze went to Kit. Then abruptly he got up, pouring the rest of his drink into a Styrofoam cup, and escorted Phyllis out of the bar.

"What's with him anyway?" Kris asked, perplexed after Ted left. "He's not himself these days. He's really falling down on the construction job at Port A. He's never there. It looks like there's going to be unscheduled delays. . . . And have you noticed how bad he looks too?"

Howard and Steve exchanged knowing glances. Then Steve gave his sister a penetrating look, which made her feel ill at ease.

She pushed her chair back from the table. "Well, I for one am finished with my drink. I'll wait for you all in the car."

Outside she paused to cover her hair with a triangular scarf, when a familiar voice—deep and vibrant—sent an electric charge coursing through her.

"I guess I owe you congratulations on your victory today," Ted said impersonally.

She turned to face him. "Why . . . why . . . thank you," she murmured. "I'm sure you realize how little I had to do with it."

"You're looking very beautiful, Kit," he said in a strangely tight voice.

"Oh . . . why . . . thank you." His compliment caught her completely off guard and she didn't know how to react. She felt flustered. She knew she was blushing furiously.

Her fingers were twisting, and untwisting the ends of scarf beneath her chin. She was no nervous she couldn't tie a simple knot.

He saw her predicament and set the ice chest he was carrying down onto the pavement beside him. "Let me help you with that," he said smoothly.

Startled, she tried to back away from him, but a parked car was directly behind her blocking her escape. He came toward her and covered her hands with his larger brown ones.

She pulled her hands quickly to her side. She felt limp and weak. He was so near. And as always his touch affected her. His long fingers were deftly securing the scarf beneath her chin.

His blue eyes on her face seemed filled with longing. She noticed that although he'd finished tying the scarf his hands lingered just for an instant at her throat in what was almost a caress.

"Kit, I never did give you . . ."

She never knew what he intended to say for Phyllis joined them at just that moment. "Ted . . . Oh . . . hi . . . Kit. Congratulations. Y'all did great!" Only the hard steel gray of her eyes belied her friendliness. "Ted, I was wondering where in the world you were. The Jarvises are on the boat, and I can't serve them drinks without that ice."

"I was just coming, Phyllis."

Phyllis slipped an arm through Ted's possessively. "See you around, Kit," the girl said in dismissal.

"Good-bye, Kit." Ted leaned over and picked up the ice chest.

"Good-bye . . ."

Kit hated herself because she'd felt so hopeful the instant before Phyllis had arrived. Ted had been so friendly, so nice. . . . She'd almost believed that he was going to ask her for an explanation of Matt's presence that night in the townhouse. She'd almost believed that such an explanation could make a difference between them. Then Phyllis had come, and Kit remembered with renewed forcefulness that he was in love with Phyllis, that he'd spent the night with her. No explanation could change the way things were between them. Her innocence was not the issue; his love for Phyllis was.

Two weeks later Ralph Jackson, Howard's younger brother, arrived to spend part of his six-week vacation with the Jacksons. Uncle Ralph was one of Kit's favorite relatives, just as she was his favorite niece.

"I don't like seeing you so depressed," he said one afternoon as they fished off the Jackson pier.

Silently she slipped a shrimp onto her hook and cast it once more into the blue-gray waters.

"I don't like being this way, but there's not much I can do about it," she replied at last, keeping her eyes glued to the bobbing cork.

"Anitra told me you were separated from your husband, that the two of you haven't been married very long."

"Uncle Ralph," she began gently, "I really don't like Mother discussing my personal problems with everyone. And I don't want to discuss them either. I'd much rather hear about Stavanger, Norway and your exciting job over there as an oil executive who's having a hand developing the North Sea."

"I thought I'd bored you silly with all that last night."

"Why did you choose overseas work . . . so late in your career?" she asked, relieved he'd let her maneuver him into a different topic of conversation.

"Now we're getting on sticky ground again—my personal problems," he replied easily. "But unlike you, I've gotten to the point where I can talk about mine. After Mary and I divorced I just wanted to get away from everything and everybody that reminded me of our life together. Stavanger is a complete change from Texas, and I was out there only a short time when I felt much better about everything."

Kit wasn't listening to Uncle Ralph any more. A change of scene . . . the idea held a strange appeal for her. If she were to leave Corpus she wouldn't be constantly running into Ted and Phyllis together. Perhaps a move would enable her to forget her problems as Uncle Ralph had forgotten his.

"I wish there was some place I could go . . . like Stavanger," she said half-aloud, half to herself.

Uncle Ralph heard her. "Are you serious? I mean *really* serious?" The sunlight was glinting in his silver hair.

"Yes." She looked up and met his direct gaze. "Oh, Uncle Ralph, I'm miserable here. I can't think of anything except . . ." Her voice broke.

"I know, honey," his voice was filled with compassion as he patted her gently on the back. "I've been there." Then in a lighter voice he said, "I seem to remember you have an accounting degree from UT?" When she nodded he continued, "I'm going to need a

170

bookkeeper for about six months. The girl who's been working for me is going to take a leave of absence because of pregnancy complications. I was planning to hire the wife of one of my other employees for the position, but if you were interested . . ."

"Oh, Uncle Ralph, thank you. It would be a life saver."

"You're sure there's no chance for you and your husband?"

"I'm sure," she whispered heavily.

Anitra and Howard were dismayed that evening at dinner when Ralph and Kit told them their news.

"Norway? But, *querida*, you haven't even tried to work things out with Ted."

"He doesn't want to work things out, Mother," Kit said firmly. "He doesn't care about me. Our marriage was a mistake from start to finish."

"You'll never make me believe that—not for one minute! Have you seen him lately? He looks broken-hearted."

Sharply: "Mother! I really don't want to talk about Ted! I've told you that before!"

"But, *querida*, if you go to Stavanger with Uncle Ralph for six months, you're sure to lose him."

"Mother!"

Conversation flowed around Kit, but she scarcely listened. After a time she became aware of her mother's voice louder than usual.

"*Querida*, your head must be in the clouds!"

"What were you saying, Mother?"

"I was talking about Marc Clay and that party he's having tomorrow night for the skippers and their crews."

"I told you before I couldn't go."

"But, *querida*, you're going to have to go—as a

special favor to your father and me. As you know Mom isn't doing at all well, and Howard has said he can fly me up to San Antonio so I can see her over the weekend. We really can't get away any other time. That means that no one from our family will be at the party to represent *Kitten*."

"What about Steve?"

"He has other plans he can't change."

"I'm not up to a party, and I'm sure Ted was invited too. I certainly don't want to risk running into him."

"From what I understand, Ted is in The Valley at his ranch," her father said. "I think you ought to go to the Clays' party. You need to get out more. And, Kitten, I know Ralph would enjoy going."

If Ted wasn't going Kit saw little harm in going herself. She did need to get out, and she knew Uncle Ralph loved parties. It would be the perfect way to entertain him.

The next evening Kit selected a floor-length gown that was a drift of lime green. The chiffonlike cloth seemed to float around her as she moved about her room getting ready for the party. She wore her black hair down about her shoulders.

After applying a soft shade of lipstick to her lips, she eyed her reflection in the mirror critically. The dress was so simple, she decided she needed to wear some jewelry. Her long, carefully manicured fingertips fingered several pieces of jewelry in her jewel case.

She lifted Ted's pearls—cool and lustrous—from black velvet and held them tentatively to her throat. The effect was stunning. Suddenly she was remembering when he'd first placed them around her neck. She'd been so much in love with him, so hopeful that their marriage would be a happy one. Just the thought of it and tears were filling her eyes.

She couldn't possibly wear them. Slowly she dropped the pearls back into the jewel case. Instead she chose a simple twist of gold and fastened it at the nape of her neck. If it wasn't as lovely as the pearls, at least the mere sight of it brought back no aching memories.

Heads turned at the party when a tall, distinguished-looking gentleman ushered his raven-haired niece through the entrance of the Clay mansion.

"Kit, darling," gushed Judith Clay, "you look stunning tonight! It's so good to see you out!"

"Judith, I'd like you to meet my Uncle Ralph . . ."

Marc Clay was hugging Kit to him and kissing her affectionately on the forehead. Then Ralph and Kit entered the living area of the house to mingle with the other guests.

The house was a perfect setting for the beautiful people who filled it. It was boldly modern in design—its living room ceiling slanting upward three stories to a sky light. Lush hanging baskets of trailing green vines hung from the high ceiling like living chandeliers. It was a house of many windows. Here one would always feel the presence of the sea.

She wandered through the house introducing Ralph to the other guests and and exchanging bits of nonsense with friends. Still clinging to Ralph, she led him onto the terrace overlooking the bay. The wind blew her hair back from her face. The house stood high upon a bluff. Some distance beneath her she watched the waves run across the soft sand and crash against the bulkhead.

Kit and Ralph stared across the bay. She pointed out the harbor bridge—a crescent of sparkling lights spanning the port area. She pointed out other landmarks and then for a time they enjoyed the view in silence. The bay was such a familiar sight; she realized she

173

would miss looking out across the water. For some inexplicable reason she thought of Ted, his handsome darkness, his smile, his touch . . . her breath caught painfully. When she left Corpus she would be leaving him as well. There would be no turning back.

Suddenly she was feeling restless—in the mood to rejoin the party, when Ralph, a social person himself, suggested that very thing. He led her back inside toward the bar where he ordered a highball for himself and a glass of Chablis for her.

The white wine relaxed her. She'd been separated from Ted for nearly a month, and this was the first time she'd felt even close to normal. Perhaps it was the wine affecting her. Perhaps it was the fact that her father had found out for certain that Ted was at his ranch and would not be returning for the party. In any event she relaxed and began to enjoy the party.

She was near the hors d'oeuvre table surveying silver dishes filled with nuts, French endive, garnished asparagus spears, avocado and chutney, crepes of all varieties, marinated carrots, and caviar. A puffy-hatted chef was cooking omelettes. She was in the process of spreading a wafer with caviar when to her horror she saw Phyllis across the room, shimmering in a gown of flowing scarlet as she stood directly beneath the floodlight at the entrance of the mansion. By her side stood Ted.

Phyllis had never looked lovelier. The red gown clung to her curves and swirled gracefully around her when she moved. Ted was casual in black slacks and a cream turtle neck.

How. . . . What . . . were they doing here?

Wafer and caviar spilled through nervous fingers to the floor, and Kit scrambled to her knees to retrieve them.

What was she going to do she wondered desperately. If only she could stay buried behind the table for the rest of the party. If only she could find some means of escape.

Her heart was thudding painfully. She was gasping as if there were no oxygen in the room. Was it always to be like this when she saw them together?

She knew suddenly that she was doing the right thing to accept the position Uncle Ralph had been kind enough to offer her. She needed to get away where there would be no danger of running into them again.

Slowly she straightened and as she did Marc Clay came to her and asked her to dance. He'd seen Ted at the door, and she knew he'd come to rescue her. The music was fast and when it stopped, they were both breathless. Marc left her safely surrounded by a cluster of friends while he went to get her a Coke.

Conversation flowed pleasantly on all sides of her. Half-listening, she nodded and murmured politely at the appropriate moments. She saw that Uncle Ralph was having the time of his life. He was on his third martini, and she knew it wasn't going to be easy to convince him to leave. And she had to convince him. She simply couldn't stay now that Ted and Phyllis were here.

Suddenly she saw Ted threading his way through the crowd and coming toward her. Smoothly he inserted himself into the conversation; just as he had smoothly inserted his own body next to hers.

Bold blue eyes fastened on her face with an intensity that she found alarming.

"Kit, would you dance this one with me?"

"Ted, I . . . I really don't think . . ." Her heart was beating so loudly and erratically she was afraid he'd hear it.

"Is it true what I just heard—that you're going to Norway to work?"

"Yes. It is."

His dark face was expressionless. "Then this might be our last chance . . . to dance together . . . to talk. . . ."

He wouldn't take no for an answer. He gripped her shaking fingers in his warm brown ones and led her out onto the dance floor. The band played a slow number, and he pulled her slender body against his. He was a flawless dancer. He held her very close, and for a time they swirled to the music. Once his thigh brushed hers, and she felt his sharp intake of breath as he paused in the middle of a dance step. Then once more his movements were fluid although he was careful not to hold her so close.

In spite of everything it felt wonderful to be in his arms once more.

"I . . . I thought you were at your ranch," she whispered.

"I was, but when I found out you were going away, I had to come back . . . to see you."

His hand pressed hers tightly, but he did not enlighten her as to why it was so important to him to see her.

She felt strangely happy, hopeful although she knew it was unreasonable to attach any significance to what he'd said.

She wished the music would go on and on and that they could dance forever, but, of course, all too soon it stopped. He led her from the dance floor, past a clump of potted palms.

"I need some fresh air, after that," he said. He pulled her by the hand out onto the terrace. Several couples had had the same idea and stood on the terrace looking out onto the bay.

"I want to talk to you," he said. "Somewhere where we can be alone . . ."

Again the madly hopeful thumping of her erratic pulsebeats.

"Ted . . . I . . ."

But he wasn't listening to her feeble protests. He was leading her down the stone steps of the terrace out onto the freshly mown lawn.

"Why don't we go for a walk on the beach?" he said.

"No . . . I really think we should go back inside."

Again he refused to listen to her protests. The lawn ended abruptly, and they stepped out onto the fifteen-foot-high seawall. Water curled and crashed beneath them. Only a few yards from them a rickety, wooden staircase descended to the beach. New lumber—doubtless intended for the construction of a new, sturdier staircase—lay in a neat pile nearby.

"Come on," he said, pulling her unresisting toward the wooden steps.

The pungent odor of salt spray and rotting sea things assailed her nostrils as she bent over and removed her green slippers. Dangling her slippers in one hand, she put a stockinged foot onto the first step of the staircase. The wind gusted and her gown was pale froth whipping around her. The step she was standing on wobbled slightly and she was glad Ted was holding her.

His eyes were again on her face; his expression was tender. His hand that was gripping hers pulled her to him tightly.

"Kit . . ."

Suddenly the lilting tones of a woman's voice sounded from behind him.

"There you are, Ted, dear," Phyllis said, her voice breathless from running. "I thought you might have come out here. Beautiful night, isn't it?"

"Yes, Phyllis, it is," Ted muttered, dropping Kit's hand and turning to include her.

"Whatever are the two of you talking about . . . and so seriously?" Phyllis queried lightly, slipping a hand through Ted's arm. Then with the savage thrust of a knife, the deceptively sweet voice continued, "Your divorce? You did say you hadn't gotten around to that yet."

Phyllis was looking directly at Kit, her gray eyes challenging, her hands clinging to Ted as if he was her exclusive property.

The horrible word so gaily spoken was pain winging swiftly and brutally through Kit. So that was why he'd wanted to see her before she left! So that was why he'd returned from his ranch! Her whole body quivered, and she lurched on the shaky staircase, losing her balance. For one horrible moment she teetered. Then she grabbed wildly for the railing, for Ted's outstretched hand, for anything that would save her from falling.

Ted was a dark blur of motion as he tried to save her, but with Phyllis clinging to him, he was not fast enough. Kit was tumbling downward. As she fell an edge of wooden stair cut into her thigh painfully. Her head hit something sharp once . . . twice. . . . Then mercifully she landed—a limp heap—on the soft, damp sand, and a wave surged and curled around her.

It seemed to her that every part of her was in pain. She was only vaguely aware of Ted rushing down the stairs after her, of him lifting her into his strong arms, of him carrying her carefully back up the stairs and into the house, of people everywhere hovering. Then there was a blackness that seemed to stretch endlessly on all sides of her.

She was aware only of a warm hand pressing hers tightly, of the comforting tones of a man's deep, resonant drawl.

Later she was still only dimly aware of being driven to the hospital emergency room, of the doctor examining her, of X-rays being taken, of a sedative to help her sleep being administered. . . .

She awoke the next morning to the indistinct, seemingly slurred tones of her mother's voice, saying gently, *"Querida,* Ted is outside. He wants to see you."

Vaguely Kit wondered what her mother was doing home from San Antonio. Then she focused on the really important thing—Ted. She couldn't see him—not this morning—not ever.

"No. . . . No . . ."

Her throbbing mind seemed fuzzy as she sat up in bed. Every part of her was aching, but one thing was clear to her. Ted belonged to Phyllis. She'd seen that so clearly last night before she'd fallen. It was something she would never lose sight of again.

"He's been here all night, *querida."*

Kit saw him then—a lean, unshaven, dark giant standing in the doorway. Just the sight of those hard, sensually virile features was torture.

"I don't care!" Kit cried desperately, bursting into tears because she knew his interest stemmed out of kindness and not love. "Tell him he can file for divorce, he can do whatever he wants . . . as long as he leaves me alone. I don't want to see him again—not ever!"

When she looked toward the door again, he was gone, and she knew he was out of her life forever.

Chapter Eleven

Kit suffered surface scratches and bruises as well as a mild concussion from her fall. Two weeks later she felt strong enough to face the task of returning to Ted's townhouse to pack her things. She'd put the task off as long as she could. It was the Thursday morning before her scheduled departure Friday afternoon for Norway.

She arrived at his townhouse in the middle of the morning. She'd selected that hour because she was sure Ted would be at work. Letting herself in with her key, she paused to survey the familiar surroundings. His usually immaculate townhouse had a littered look. Beer cans were everywhere. Cigarettes overflowed from ashtrays. She remembered Ted had quit smoking when he'd been at the university.

Well, it was obvious he was enjoying himself, she thought without bitterness. She wanted his happiness more than anything. He was probably enjoying the freedom of being a bachelor again. She imagined him partying and entertaining Phyllis late into his nights.

She went to the master bedroom and began packing. He'd thoughtfully grouped all her belongings into one closet. When her suitcases were neatly packed, she closed their lids. If only she could organize her life as neatly as she'd organized her suitcases. If only she could tear the pain in her heart out and pack it away.

She sank down onto the bed. How would she ever get over him—even in Norway? Since she'd moved out, it hurt her more every day to be away from him. But she had to let him have the woman he really loved. She'd thought of calling him and trying to explain about Matt before she left, but always the thought that it was easier for Ted if she didn't, stopped her. This way, believing the worst about her, he could live his life with Phyllis free of guilt. By not calling him, she was making it easier for him to do what he really wanted to do.

She remembered the sight of him holding Phyllis in his arms on their wedding night, the sight of Phyllis on his arm, lovely in swirling red the night she herself had fallen. Phyllis and he belonged together. Above everything Kit wanted his happiness, even if his happiness could not include her.

The lock of the suitcase snapped, and Kit dragged it from the bedroom. She went back for the second suitcase.

She heard the front door open and as she stepped into the living room, her own eyes locked with the frostiest of gray eyes.

"What are you doing here?" Phyllis demanded in a possessive tone. From her attitude it was clear she felt she belonged and Kit did not.

"I was just leaving. I came for my things."

"I hope you're gone before Ted comes home. The

last thing he needs is to see you again before you leave. He's been so happy ever since you moved out."

"Has he?"

"Yes. I saw from the beginning that you were no good. Not for him or for Missy."

"Well, as I already know how you feel about me, I don't see any point in going over all of it again," Kit said quietly. "Whether you believe it or not I want Ted to be happy."

"I'm glad you called that night. I'm glad you found out all about . . ."

She never finished what she was going to say, for she heard a sound at the door directly behind her. She turned and stared open-mouthed at Ted, who was standing in the doorway.

His haggard features seemed chiseled from granite; his mouth was a thin, hard line. Just the sight of him was searing, bittersweet pain to Kit.

"Finish what you were going to say, Phyllis," he said in a dangerously quiet voice.

"I . . . I . . . don't know what I would have said," she stammered.

"I think you do."

"It wasn't anything important. If you don't mind I have to go now." She picked up a brown sack on the coffee table. "Missy forgot her lunch when she was over here this morning, and I promised her I'd come pick it up for her. If you don't mind," she said, edging past him, "I need to get it to her. You know how early they eat. I would hate for her to be left out."

"When you get back, Phyllis, you and I are going to have a long talk."

He turned to Kit. He was studying her with an intensity that jarred every nerve end in her slender body.

182

"I was just on my way out when Phyllis came in," Kit said weakly. "I didn't think you'd be home at this hour—you remember you asked me to come by when you wouldn't be here. I'm sorry if I've inconvenienced you."

She strained against the handle of the heavy suitcase, trying to pick it up. He was at her side in an instant. His long brown fingers covered hers as he took the suitcase from her. As always his touch was electric, and she jumped back.

"I'll carry this to your car in a minute," he said. "But first I'd like to talk to you."

"I can't imagine that we have anything more to say to one another," she whispered shakily.

"Perhaps we can start with what Phyllis was saying when I came in here just a minute ago. What did she mean when she said she was glad you'd called her and found about . . . about what?"

"It doesn't matter now, Ted. I . . . I have to go." The muscles of her throat constricted with the tension of being too near him. She had to get away. But that was impossible because Ted's hand was suddenly on her arm, stopping what would have been her swift retreat with the punishing grip of his strong fingers.

"If it doesn't matter then you shouldn't mind telling me," he said simply, leading her to the couch.

She sat down and he sat across from her, and she was very aware of him—so close—of the coiled strength of his powerful body which he would unleash if she tried to escape him again. She had no choice but to give him the answers he required.

"Well . . . the night . . . the night when you found me here with Matt . . ." she faltered. His face darkened only slightly at the mention of Matt. She thought he strained for control. "I was worried when I got home from the party and couldn't find you. I thought maybe something had happened to you, so I called Phyllis. She said you were asleep over there. I knew then for sure that what I'd suspected all along was true—that it was over between you and me, that you loved her. It was the past repeating itself."

He leaned forward in his chair, his blue eyes blazing. His dark face was amazement.

"Phyllis let you think . . ." She nodded mutely. "You thought I loved Phyllis . . . all along?" he repeated slowly, as if he needed to say it carefully to get used to the idea.

"Yes. What I don't understand is why you married me when you loved her. It really wasn't fair of you."

"And your thinking this bothered you from the start of our marriage?" His deep voice sounded suddenly eager, and an answering eagerness leaped in her.

"From the first day."

"Why didn't you tell me?"

"Because I knew you'd tell me a lie."

"Why would you think I'd lie? Did I ever lie to you before?"

"Yes, in a way."

It was strange but now that their marriage was over she could talk about hurts she'd kept bottled inside of her for a very long time.

"You said something about the past repeating itself. What did you mean by that? And I'd like to know . . . specifically . . . when I lied to you?" he said quietly.

"That night—the last night I saw you—five years ago, the night I ran out when you tried to make love to me. . . . Well, I called you back that night, Ted. Letitia answered the phone. She asked me if I really wanted to disturb you—that you were in bed. I knew then that you really didn't care for me in the same way that I cared for you if you could go from me to her so quickly. What you felt was merely physical. I was hurt, and I never wanted to see you again."

"Letitia!" he spoke her name in savage anger. "I can believe she did that—after living with her two and a half years. She had a vindictive streak. I only married her out of loneliness. You'd left me and she was going through a rough time herself. Dad died and I really wasn't thinking too clearly." He paused. "Kit, you can call Marc Clay and ask him to confirm what I'm going to tell you. Letitia and Marc came by after you left that night to copy my notes. Marc and I had a law class together. He'd skipped a class or something—I'm not too sure now. You'd run out on me that night and wouldn't even answer the phone when I called you. I was in no mood for company so I told them I was tired and went to bed. I'm telling you the truth, Kit. I swear it." He hesitated. "And to think . . . all those years I thought you'd left me for Rodney. That's why I couldn't trust you."

She knew intuitively he was telling the truth, but this knowledge gave her no joy. The past was over. He loved Phyllis now.

"I *was* asleep at Phyllis's the night you called," he continued. "But it wasn't like it sounds. I'd gotten home shortly after twelve-thirty. Her light was on. I went over and we got to talking. I must have fallen asleep—goodness, I was dead tired that night. At the party I'd tried to get your attention at midnight to tell you I felt like a walking zombie and was ready to leave. But you wouldn't speak to me. Anyway, when the phone rang, I woke up and found myself sprawled on her couch covered with blankets. I got up and came home. That's when I found you with Matt. I was hardly rational at the time."

"Why were you standing on the seawall holding Phyllis in your arms on our wedding night?" she asked, determined to know everything. "When I asked you where you'd gone you said you'd gone for a walk."

"Ah. . . . So you saw us then. Kit, you must have realized how much Phyllis dislikes the idea of your being married to me. She and I are extremely close. She turned to me and Missy when her sister died. She can't accept that Letitia is dead, and that I need to live my own life. That night I was trying to persuade her to give you a chance, but she wouldn't listen to me. I didn't want to discuss it with you on our wedding night. I knew you'd be upset . . ."

"You aren't in love with Phyllis?"

"We are close friends. That's all. Kit,, you have to believe me. She dislikes you out of loyalty to her sister. That's all."

"Oh."

She'd been so wrong about him. If only she'd had the courage to ask him these things before she'd ruined her chance to be happy with him. But now he believed she was the type of woman who chased after men and brought them home to bed.

As if he read her mind: "Kit, I never did give you a chance to explain about Matt. What was he doing here at four in the morning?"

"He'd insisted on driving me home because he said I was in no condition to drive. He only stayed because I was so frantic when I couldn't find you. I was in his arms because he was comforting me after I learned you were asleep at Phyllis's."

"And that time Rodney was in the store holding you . . ."

"He really was getting an eyelash out of my eye. I'd been crying because I'd seen you holding Phyllis on our

186

wedding night. I didn't want to explain that to him so I told him I had something in my eye."

"So that's what you were holding back. . . . It seems we've been at cross purposes, you and I. You thought I loved Phyllis, and I didn't realize you loved me. When all the time I thought you knew how much I loved you."

"What?" Her voice sounded curiously light and breathless.

"Why did you think I married you?"

"I didn't know. You certainly never said you loved me."

"Then I should have, but I was too proud, and you seemed so cold." He spanned the short distance between them, and took her in his arms. "Kit, I've been such a fool. Yes, I loved you. I always have. When I read in the newspaper about Rodney jilting you, I went over to your house hoping to see you. In spite of everything I'd never forgotten you. I hardly ever check those tents myself—you know that. Then you came out—all haughty and disdainful—and ordered me to the servants' entrance as if I weren't as good as you. I remembered all the old grievances against you. That's why I kissed you—to teach you a lesson, but the lesson backfired. You kissed me so passionately—as though you still cared. After that kiss I couldn't get you out of my mind. I went down to the club determined never to think of you again, but then you came down yourself. After you wrecked *Wild Lady,* and I saw you in the water and in danger, I knew then how much I loved you. When your father asked me to dinner, I had to come. I *had* to see you. When you weren't wearing Rodney's ring, I thought there might be a chance for us. I thought if I could persuade you to marry me, you might come to love me in time. Then you said you'd marry me on the condition that I not touch you. That month before we married was the longest in my life. I knew if I saw very much of you, I couldn't keep my promise, and you might not marry me. That's why I went out of town. Then after we got married. . . . Well, you know what a thorough mess I made of our marriage. . . . I wouldn't really blame you if you hated me."

"Oh, Ted I couldn't hate you," she said in her softest voice. "I love you. I always have."

For a long moment his eyes filled with wonder then his lips covered hers and lingered in a passionate kiss that left them both breathless. After a long time his mouth left hers.

"When I learned from your father you were going away, I drove ninety miles an hour to get to the Clays' party. I wanted to give you a chance to explain about Matt. But I never got the chance. After you fell, and you sent me away. . . . I thought I'd lost you."

"I only sent you away because I thought you loved Phyllis. I thought you wanted to talk about divorce."

"These past few weeks when I was sure I'd lost you have been a living nightmare for me. I even took up smoking again," he murmured. "I haven't eaten; I've hardly been able to work."

"It's been just as bad for me. I wanted to call you before I went away, but I didn't think you'd want me to."

"Kit, darling, we've been such fools."

Again his lips covered hers urgently. "But we have the rest of our lives to make up for it," he continued.

Her fingers reached up and combed his auburn hair. "Would it be too soon if we began now?" she asked tremulously.

A wicked light danced in his blue eyes and a strange

rippling excitement coursed through her in response. He curved a finger under her chin and tilted her head up to his. His lips found hers again.

"I love you," she whispered against his mouth.

"And I love you, my darling *Wild Lady,* and always will."

Silhouette ❤ *Romance*

15-Day Free Trial Offer
6 Silhouette Romances

6 Silhouette Romances, free for 15 days! We'll send you 6 new Silhouette Romances to keep for 15 days, absolutely free! If you decide not to keep them, send them back to us. You pay nothing.

Free Home Delivery. But if you enjoy them as much as we think you will, keep them by paying us the retail price of just $1.50 each. We'll pay all shipping and handling charges. You'll then automatically become a member of the Silhouette Book Club, and will receive 6 more new Silhouette Romances every month and a bill for $9.00. That's the same price you'd pay in the store, but you get the convenience of home delivery.

Read every book we publish. The Silhouette Book Club is the way to make sure you'll be able to receive every new romance we publish.

This offer expires January 31, 1982

IT'S YOUR OWN SPECIAL TIME

Contemporary romances for today's women.
Each month, six very special love stories will be yours
from SILHOUETTE.
Look for them wherever books are sold
or order now from the coupon below.

$1.50 each

Silhouette Romance

___#55 WINTER'S HEART Ladame
___#56 RISING STAR Trent
___#57 TO TRUST TOMORROW John
___#58 LONG WINTER'S NIGHT Stanford
___#59 KISSED BY MOONLIGHT Vernon
___#60 GREEN PARADISE Hill
___#61 WHISPER MY NAME Michaels
___#62 STAND-IN BRIDE Halston
___#63 SNOWFLAKES IN THE SUN Brent
___#64 SHADOW OF APOLLO Hampson
___#65 A TOUCH OF MAGIC Hunter
___#66 PROMISES FROM THE PAST Vitek
___#67 ISLAND CONQUEST Hastings
___#68 THE MARRIAGE BARGAIN Scott
___#69 WEST OF THE MOON St. George
___#70 MADE FOR EACH OTHER Afton Bonds
___#71 A SECOND CHANCE ON LOVE Ripy
___#72 ANGRY LOVER Beckman
___#73 WREN OF PARADISE Browning

___#74 WINTER DREAMS Trent
___#75 DIVIDE THE WIND Carroll
___#76 BURNING MEMORIES Hardy
___#77 SECRET MARRIAGE Cork
___#78 DOUBLE OR NOTHING Oliver
___#79 TO START AGAIN Halldorson
___#80 WONDER AND WILD DESIRE Stephens
___#81 IRISH THOROUGHBRED Roberts
___#82 THE HOSTAGE BRIDE Dailey
___#83 LOVE LEGACY Halston
___#84 VEIL OF GOLD Vitek
___#85 OUTBACK SUMMER John
___#86 THE MOTH AND THE FLAME Adams
___#87 BEYOND TOMORROW Michaels
___#88 AND THEN CAME DAWN Stanford
___#89 A PASSIONATE BUSINESS James
___#90 WILD LADY Major
___#91 WRITTEN IN THE STARS Hunter
___#92 DESERT DEVIL McKay
___#93 EAST OF TODAY Browning

- -

SILHOUETTE BOOKS. Department SB/1
1230 Avenue of the Americas
New York, NY 10020

Please send me the books I have checked above. I am enclosing
$_____ (please add 50¢ to cover postage and handling. NYS and
NYC residents please add appropriate sales tax). Send check or
money order—no cash or C.O.D.'s please. Allow six weeks for delivery.

NAME_____

ADDRESS_____

CITY_____STATE/ZIP_____